THE
KATE GREENAWAY
TREASURY

THE
Kate Greenaway Treasury

Introduction by RUTH HILL VIGUERS

An Anthology of the
Illustrations and Writings
of Kate Greenaway,
Edited and Selected by
EDWARD ERNEST,
Assisted by Patricia Tracy Lowe

The World Publishing Company · Cleveland and New York

ACKNOWLEDGMENTS

The editor and The World Publishing Company herewith render thanks to the following publishers and individuals whose interest, co-operation, and permission to reprint have made possible the preparation of *The Kate Greenaway Treasury*. All possible care has been taken to trace ownership of every selection included and to make full acknowledgment for its use. If any errors have accidentally occurred, they will be corrected in subsequent editions, provided notification is sent to the publishers.

Frederick Warne & Co., Ltd., London for excerpts from "A Century of Kate Greenaway" by Anne Carroll Moore, from *The House of Warne: 100 Years of Publishing*.

Frederick Warne & Co., Ltd., London, for illustrations on front and back endpapers and on pages 12, 19, 43, 74, 87, and 100 of this book from *Kate Greenaway Pictures* (with an introduction by H.M. Cundall).

Frederick Warne & Co., Ltd., London, for excerpts on pages 174–177 of this book from *Kate Greenaway's Book of Painting*.

Frederick Warne & Co., Ltd., London, for excerpts on pages 301–314 of this book from *Kate Greenaway's Book of Games*.

The estate of Dr. Percy Spielmann for "A Biographical Sketch" and "Artist and Critic," excerpted and adapted from *Kate Greenaway* by M.H. Spielmann and G.S. Layard, published by Adam and Charles Black, London, 1905.

Mr. Robert Partridge, of London, for helpful advice in assembling bibliographical information.

Published by The World Publishing Company
2231 West 110th Street, Cleveland, Ohio 44102
Library of Congress catalog card number: 67-23363
The special contents of this book copyright © 1967 by
The World Publishing Company. All rights reserved. No part of this book may be reproduced in any form without written permission from the publisher, except for brief passages included in a review appearing in a newspaper or magazine. Printed in the United States of America.
Typographic design by Mina Baylis

A note on spelling: Where material is of American origin, American spelling and punctuation have been used in this book. Many portions of this book are facsimile reproductions of original works by Kate Greenaway and others, originally published in England. Spelling in these portions naturally follows British usage. British spelling has also been retained in the excerpts from M.S. Spielmann and G. S. Layard.

CONTENTS

UNDER THE WINDOW,

written and illustrated
by Kate Greenaway
Published 1878. *Selections.* 103

BIRTHDAY BOOK,

Verses by Mrs. Sale Barker,
illustrated by Kate Greenaway.
Published 1880.
Selections from all the months. 122

MOTHER GOOSE,
   traditional rhymes, illustrated
   by Kate Greenaway.
   Published 1881. *Selections.*

Rock-a-Bye, Baby
Little Lad, Little Lad
There Was an Old Woman
Elsie Marley
Johnny Shall Go to the Fair
Jack and Jill
Girls and Boys, Come Out to Play
Little Betty Blue
Billy Boy Blue
Little Jumping Joan
Ride a Cock-horse
Humpty Dumpty
Tom, Tom, the Piper's Son
Ring-a-Ring-a-Roses
Goosey, Goosey, Gander
Polly, Put the Kettle On

A DAY IN A CHILD'S LIFE,

   poems, set to music
   by Myles B. Foster,
   illustrated by Kate Greenaway.
   Published 1881. *Complete.*

Waking, A. MARRYAT
The Lesson, ANON
Playtime, W. HAMILTON

Grace Before Meals, R. HERRICK
A Song of a Doll, CHARLES KINGSLEY
A Romp, M.B. FOSTER
Tired, SOMERVILLE GIBNEY
Child's Prayer, M. L. DUNCAN
Sleeping, ANON

THE
KATE GREENAWAY
TREASURY

Kate Greenaway

INTRODUCTION

N THE practice of art, as in every human activity, each generation learns from the generations that have gone before. The lesser artists will imitate. The greater ones will turn to their forerunners not to find models but to start reverberations in their own imaginations. Among these a few may become the originals of their generation. Kate Greenaway was one of these. Highly successful in England, recognized in France, Germany, and North America, she became a vogue. When even the clothes in which she dressed her figures became the fashion for children of the period, it was not surprising that aspiring artists should imitate her technique, her designs, and her style. But Kate Greenaway was giving in her pictures "not what she saw, but what she felt, even as she looked." The instinctive feeling in her pictures could not be assumed by copyists.

Great art enlarges the capacity of the beholder—or listener or reader —to experience life in all its variety. Each original voice, each fresh vision, adds a new dimension to artistic encounters. Every new human spirit should have access to many avenues that may delight him and lead him further.

The work of the three great English picture-book artists of the nineteenth century represents the best to be found in picture books for children in any era: the strength of design and richness of color and detail of Walter Crane's pictures; the eloquence, humor, vitality, and movement of Randolph Caldecott's art; and the tenderness, dignity, and grace of the very personal interpretation of Kate Greenaway's enchanted land of childhood.

In a time when children's picture books exist in large numbers and great variety, we need reminders of the art that has contributed to the present wealth. Even more important, we need reminders of work that, even after nearly a hundred years, still speaks to children, lest children of our time be deprived of an important heritage.

In Kate Greenaway's garden the sun is always shining. We look at her pictures much as we look at a blossoming garden, seeing only the light on the flowers, forgetting the rain or the toil that went into the creation of that beauty. Her drawings show color, humor, grace, but no hint of the effort and drudgery inevitable in the giving of form to vision.

That Kate Greenaway deserved the fame she attained can be seen by the reproductions of her paintings, drawings, and sketches in this volume; her fame actually rested on her illustrations for relatively few books. A bibliography of those she illustrated that children of later generations have loved and that future generations will be most likely to enjoy would be short: a book of games; a birthday book; a collection of Mother Goose rhymes; a unique picture book *The Pied Piper of Hamelin*; *The Language of Flowers* and *A Day in a Child's Life*, both distinguished for their exquisite flower pictures; and two graceful books of her own verses. Her tiny *Almanacks* are quite perfect little treasures, but appreciation of them is limited chiefly to collectors. The storybooks by other authors that she illustrated and the collection of rhymes by Ann and Jane Taylor are, in their texts, sentimental or didactic, with little appeal to later generations.

Yet every book containing her pictures is enhanced—even one of mincing verse or spurious prose—by the purity of her vision of childhood. She stands with Walter Crane and Randolph Caldecott. They are the three artists who first gave young children well-drawn illustrations in handsomely designed books. She stands with them, and she shared with them the skill of the inspired artist-engraver who encouraged and supported them and turned their drawings into picture books.

She stands also by herself. Kate Greenaway was an innovator who brought to her pictures of flowers and flowerlike children a freshness that none of her many imitators could capture.

Her childhood stayed with her always. "I had such a very happy time when I was a child," she said, and she marveled that although they had the same surroundings, her brother and sisters were not so happy as she.

I suppose my imaginary life made me one long continuous joy—filled everything with a strange wonder and beauty. Living in that childish wonder is a most beautiful feeling—I can so well remember it. There was always

On a letter to Ruskin

something more—behind and beyond everything—to me; the golden spectacles were very big.

It is that "behind and beyond" that one feels in her pictures which gives them their depth and an indefinable essence.

No doubt "the latent artistic emotion with which she had been endowed at birth" was the source of the intensity of her feelings—"the wildness of her own enjoyments and the bitterness of her own disappointments"—which etched each experience indelibly on her memory.

Children's lives are a series of first experiences, the experiences most likely to make lasting impressions. Even what seems to adults to be commonplace may offer wonder to the young child. But the wonder fades with repetition of the experience unless imagination is aroused. The most blessed of the artists and poets can give to children experiences that start imaginations growing. Kate Greenaway is one of these. She is unique in that the most beautiful impressions of her childhood not only became part of the woman but remained in her memory so clearly as to be essential in the expression of the artist. This expression, endowing childhood and the actions, moods, and games of childhood with the beauty she felt, is a rightful inheritance of each new generation.

The little girls whom Anne Carroll Moore observed on a New York sidewalk, seated at a grocery packing case, *living* the picture of a Kate Greenaway tea party, are characteristic of all children whose first experiences at home, at school, in a vacant lot, a garden, or on a city street, at play or in books have given them the beginning of the power to realize far more than the eye can see.

Austin Dobson once said of Kate Greenaway's work,

I can't help thinking that I should have been a better man if I had had such pleasant play-books in my inartistic childhood.

Although she often visited the country and the seashore, most of Kate Greenaway's life was spent in London, but the happy days on a farm at Rolleston in Nottinghamshire during her early childhood remained in her heart and in her memory. Scenes from her childhood reflected in her picture books—fields of cowslips, a carpet of daisies and grass, primroses dotting a hilltop, a cluster of dandelions beside a stream, and blossoming apple trees—were as present to her and gave her as much delight as the roses in a London garden. And her eyes were open to beauty everywhere.

Poor weeds—fine tall fresh green thistles and docks spreading out their leaves in lovely curves. I'm sorry for all the things that are not much wanted on the earth.—And long ago, I loved docks; we used to play with the seeds and pretend it was tea. We used to have a tea-shop and weigh it out and sell it for tea. Perhaps docks do not mean that for anyone else in the world—like the purple mallow and the seeds I used to call cheeses, sweet little fat green things, do you know?

The elder Greenaways saw to it that their children had opportunity to develop their natural gifts. It must have been a great satisfaction to John Greenaway, a highly respected artist and engraver, that one child should demonstrate a talent for drawing. Her artistic education began early, and from the age of twelve she won awards and prizes. Her greatest good fortune was, however, to be recognized by the color printer Edmund Evans, who had been responsible for enlisting Walter Crane and Randolph Caldecott in the creating of picture books for children.

She had achieved some success with her valentines and Christmas cards but had received little encouragement for her verses, which she believed to be appropriate vehicles for her illustrations. Mr. Evans saw

"The Bubble"

See the pretty planet!
Floating sphere!
Faintest breeze will fan it
Far or near.

merit in Kate Greenaway's verses and genius in her drawings and purchased her first collection for a book. He engraved wood blocks—including separate color blocks—and printed an edition of *Under the Window* that the publishers considered foolishly large for so expensive a book. But his faith in the success of Kate Greenaway's work was more than vindicated. Reprinting continued up to 70,000 copies, and French and German editions increased this number by more than 30,000.

From a greeting-card artist she became a book illustrator, an artist of childhood for children. Quaint though her children are—charmingly dressed in a costume of many years before her own birth—they are truly children, alive, moving, their faces solemn with the natural intentness of young children at play. What could be more real than the concentration of the little boy blowing his penny trumpet for the children dancing on the curve of the hill in *Under the Window*? Or more characteristic than the picture in the same book of girls at tea, playing most seriously at being grown-up ladies?

When a critic called the expression on her children's faces woebegone, Kate Greenaway agreed that it was absurd for children to be playing a game and for their faces to be "plunged in the deepest despair and sadness," and she said that she hoped to do better. Few have been troubled by mournfulness in the children of her pictures, however. In only one of her books—*Little Ann and other Poems* by Ann and Jane Taylor—are faces truly melancholy. The tears that flow, decorously wiped away with white handkerchiefs (for all the world as though the children were playing at being sad), or the mouths that droop are but extensions of the painful subject of remorse for misbehavior expressed in the poems. In her *Book of Games* and in her other books, if the faces appear solemn, they are also pleasant and unself-conscious. Kate Greenaway children have the rapt faces natural to those children who are uninterrupted in their absorption with a world of wonders they are only beginning to discover or experience.

The artist Kate Greenaway can be known by her books, her paintings, and her drawings. Far too little has been available about the woman. Inclusion in this book of material from *Kate Greenaway* by M. H. Spielmann and G. S. Layard, which has long been out of print, makes possible acquaintance with a warm, gifted person. She was frequently called strong-minded, determined—qualities she certainly showed in the care with which she did everything and in her faithfulness to her own vision. She cared that her friends should like her pictures, she felt criticism and tried to analyze its justification, and she kept on being herself.

Success brought suggestions from many people that she do different things—life-sized pictures, etchings, small pictures, landscapes—and her humor came to the fore: "The man with the donkey who tried to please everybody is nothing to it!"

Disliking the clothes worn by children of her time, she turned to an earlier period, choosing a costume that had simplicity and grace, making the costumes, and dressing her child models in them so that she could study them on living, moving figures.

She enjoyed children and understood them, never forcing herself upon them, but responding so naturally that one of the Locker-Lampson children could write her, "It was such tremendous fun having you here, and you so enter into our roystering spirits." She endured the squirming and even the chatter of her restless little sitters as she tried to concentrate on her work. She knew what children liked in pictures and stories; and she knew they did not care "about children in an abstract . . . way. That belongs to older people." Although her pictured children, with their quaint dress and flowerlike faces, may appear like figures in an exquisite dream, each new generation sees them as real children. They have none of the coyness, the self-conscious parody of childhood of which many lesser artists are guilty.

Seldom does one find an indoor scene among Kate Greenaway's paintings and illustrations. There are some early sketches of interiors of the cottage at Rolleston, and there is the beautiful portrait of Thomas Chappell with the warm brick of the farm kitchen behind him; but such pictures are few. Her children are almost always out-of-doors. They walk on a village street, dance, sing, fish from a bridge, play on the grass of a meadow or a garden, parade in graceful processions in the sunlight. If they have a tea party it is under the trees. The closest they come to a house is the doorstep.

It is characteristic that she once expressed disappointment in the Tate Gallery, saying that she preferred the "going out and coming in" to the gallery itself.

There's the beautiful river and the boats and the opposite shore of wharves and buildings, and I felt how nice it must be at Venice to come out and find the sea—I do like the sea—or a large river to every town.

She was aware of beauty everywhere. In a letter to Frederick Locker

A birthday garland for John Ruskin

she once asked, "What do you think—is it not a beautiful world? . . . have I got a defective faculty that few things are ugly to me?"

She loved people, bands, the ring of the muffin bell, the flower sellers, the fruit stalls, and the sound of church bells. She found the "cheerful streets" a rest after enough of silence.

And to John Ruskin she once said:

I go on liking things more and more, seeing them more and more beautiful. Don't you think it is a great possession to be able to get so much joy out of things that are always there to give it, and do not change? What a great pity my hands are not clever enough to do what my mind and eyes see, but there it is!

Always modest about her own work, and admiring the work of others, she was genuinely eager to improve, asking for criticism and taking it seriously. Frederick Locker wrote reassuringly to her, telling her not to be downhearted about her art, nor to "feel depressed when you gaze

19

at Crane's reproductions. Each has his or her merit, and there is room for all." Another time he admonished her,

You must be influenced by what the critics say up to a certain point—but not beyond. It is very annoying to be misunderstood and to see critics trying to show off their own cleverness, but you are now paying the penalty of *success*. . . . I *quite* feel what you say about Ruskin. There *does* seem to be a "holiness" about his words and ideas. . . . His opinion is worth all the commonplace critics put together, and worth more than the opinion of nineteen out of twenty Royal Academicians.

After she became acquainted with John Ruskin he wanted to see everything she did.

If I don't like it—the public will—if I do there's always one more pleasure in my disconsolate old life. And you ought to feel that when I do like it—nobody likes it so much!—nor half nor a quarter so much.

He believed in her so intensely and expected so much of her that he was often harshly honest in his criticism, challenging her to draw *things* as they are—rocks, sods, trees, feet. He wrote to her,

I want you to go to Boulogne and take a course of fishwives and wading children. . . . I want the blue of the sea for you, and the running action of the bare feet.

But he could say of her:

The fairyland that she creates for you is not beyond the sky nor beneath sea, but near you, even at your own doors. She does but show you how to see it.

"Calm in a Teacup"

That she had taught him how to see it is evident in his words:

> I saw a boy in a brown jacket with a yellow basket in his hand—looking up wistfully at the sky—in the main street of Worcester—he wanted only a Kate to draw him and would have been immortal.

In a series of lectures that John Ruskin gave at Oxford on the art of England, he included a lecture on Kate Greenaway. While he saw her faults, he also recognized her originality and her peculiar genius. "How dogged the English are," he once said, "in thinking that you can't praise anybody honestly."

If knowledge of her shortcomings depressed her, Ruskin's praise could lift her spirits:

> You are fast becoming—I believe you are already, except only Edward B. Jones—the helpfullest in showing me that there are yet living souls on earth who can see beauty and peace and Good-will among men—and rejoice in them.

And once the expression of his praise was in the very spirit of her vision:

> . . . I think you never did a more marvellous piece of beauty and it's a treasure to me like a caught dream.

His advice to her on learning perspective could be taken with benefit by workers in any of the arts:

> One never *uses* the rules, one only feels them—and defies if one likes. . . . But we should first know and enjoy them.

In one of his last letters to her he spoke again of her book that had delighted him most:

> . . . of course the Piper is the best book you ever did—the Piper himself unsurpassable—and I feel as if he had piped me back out of the hill again, and would give some spring times yet to rejoice in your lovely work and its witness to them.

The friendship, criticism, support, and stimulation that Ruskin gave her, chiefly through his letters, was abundantly repaid by her friendship and her generous gift of time and talent during his last ten years of growing infirmity. His letters ceased in the spring of 1889, but until his death in January 1900 and although she herself was far from well, Kate Greenaway wrote to him almost daily. She kept a letter to him on her desk, adding to it, whenever she had a moment, whatever she thought

21

would interest him and often illustrating the letter with sketches. As soon as a page was filled she posted it. She told him about pictures she had seen in galleries and exhibitions, about books she was reading, about the adventures and misadventures of her elderly dog Rover, and the funny sayings of her little models. Occasionally a note of her own longings crept in, as when she wrote of reading a little of Browning every night and liking each poem better with every reading.

> That fires me with ambition to try to write something, and I do try, and they won't come good; isn't it hateful of them to be so poor and weak? But I am going to try more than ever, and I'm going to try other things too if only I can keep well. I do mean to try and do a little more in my life. I'm not content, for I have not yet *expressed myself*. It's such a queer feeling, that longing to express yourself and not finding a means or a way— yet it goads you on and won't let you rest.

Notebooks filled with rough drafts of poems, from which she intended eventually to select the best to put into good form, testify to her longing to write true poetry. She realized with regret that she would never attain this ambition. Nevertheless, her verses for children are in complete harmony with her drawings. They are unpretentious, amusing, sometimes touched with surprise or mystery, and true to the feelings of childhood. They give evidence that although she lacked the power of great poetic expression, she had, in Austin Dobson's words, "the root of the matter in her." She may have had more influence than she knew: Robert Louis Stevenson was inspired by her verses in the *Birthday Book* to try his own hand at writing verse for children.

She began painting in oil while she was often ill, just two years before her death. In her letters to Ruskin she gave him frequent accounts first of her discouragement, and then of her growing pleasure in the medium that was new to her.

> Perhaps I have hopes of the capacity of oil paint that won't be realized, but it is nice to get a medium to work in that does what you want more at once. I don't like small oil things half as much as water-colours—but I do lose the *go* of things in water-colours.

Another time she wrote,

> I am rather liking red and blue just now. I suppose it is the winter makes all faint colours look so pale. I like the strong warm colours of scarlet— it is nice to do. I always like painting fur, which I think is rather curious, for I don't like painting hair and never do it well.

22

And later,

> I begin to make the flesh look like flesh and no longer white and chalky.
> I like doing it so much and if only the models would not talk so much! . . .
> I can't see why they want to talk so and never think. How funny it would
> be to have a mind that never liked to be alone with its own thoughts.

In trying to define what she believed art—in painting—to be, Kate
Greenaway said,

> It isn't realism, it isn't all imagination, it's a queer giving something to
> nature that is possible for nature to have, but always has not.

It was thus she used her exquisite flowers, not for their beauty alone but
for their place in the creating of a lovely design—a blossoming branch
curving over a girl's head, a cluster of red roses adding a note of deep
color to a delicate composition.

> I like making cowslip fields grow [she once said] and apple-trees bloom at
> a moment's notice. This is what it is, you see, to have gone through life
> with an enchanted land ever beside you.

After visiting an art gallery, Kate Greenaway once wrote of feeling
so much better for having seen the pictures: "I always do, if I can see
a beautiful thing." And later,

> You live in a great many places at once, don't you, when you have beauti-
> ful pictures hanging on your walls? You lift up your eyes and you are
> away in a new land in a moment.

The children who have glimpsed, when they are young, Kate Greenaway's enchanted land may have added to their most private gallery
of beautiful pictures many that can transport them at will to a new
land—to Kate Greenaway's garden where the sun is shining.

RUTH HILL VIGUERS

Wellesley, Massachusetts

KATE GREENAWAY

A Biographical Sketch

WHY HAS the name of Kate Greenaway, artist and illustrator, been a household word in Great Britain and abroad for nearly one hundred years? Mainly, she drew Christmas and valentine cards, illustrated a score or two of "toy-books," and produced a number of dainty water-colour drawings and portraits. But she is judged, not by the dignity of her materials, or by the area of her canvas, but by the originality of her genius and by the strength and depth of the impression she has stamped on the mind and sentiment of the world. Her success rests on the universal appeal she made, almost unconsciously, to the human heart. To use the words of her biographers, M. H. Spielmann and G. S. Layard, she was the interpreter-in-chief of childhood. As Holman Hunt, Millais, and their associates invigorated the art of England by their foundation of the Pre-Raphaelite Brotherhood, so Kate Greenaway introduced a Pre-Raphaelite spirit into the art of the nursery.

Randolph Caldecott and Walter Crane, illustrators of books for children at the same time as Kate Greenaway, aimed at interesting children in their drawings; but Kate Greenaway interested us in the children themselves. She taught us more of the charm of their ways than we had seen before; she showed us their graces, their little foibles, their thousand little prettinesses, the sweet little characteristics and psychology of their tender age as no one else had done before.

Kate Greenaway was born at 1, Cavendish Street, Hoxton (London), on the 17th day of March 1846. She was the daughter of Elizabeth Jones and John Greenaway, a prominent wood-engraver and draughtsman, whose work is to be found in the yearly volumes of the *Illustrated*

London News and *Punch*, and in the leading magazines and books of the day.

The family consisted of Elizabeth Mary (Lizzie), afterwards Mrs. Frank Coxall, born in 1841; Catherine (Kate), born in 1846; Frances Rebecca (Fanny) born in 1850; and Alfred John, born in 1852.

A few years before her death Kate Greenaway conceived the idea of writing the autobiography of her childhood; but she only left behind a long detailed record of undigested recollections and her sensations in recalling them. Clearly, her early capacity for accurate observation, ravenously seizing upon and making her own the infinitely little details of her childish experiences, was an important factor in her artistic development, and her descriptions of her childhood illustrate well how impressions absorbed in early years coloured the artist's performances in far-off days to come.

Kate's early life was uneventful. But because of her autobiographical notes, we are fortunate in possessing records concerning this period from the pen of the artist herself, candid and direct, and as particular in detail as if studied with her eye at the microscope of memory.

When Kate was not yet two she was taken, because of her mother's illness, to live at Rolleston, in Nottinghamshire. Here began her relationship with the countryside and her intimacy with more or less unsophisticated nature—a love which was her prevailing passion throughout her life. After a year or two in the country, Kate moved back to London with her family. Because John Greenaway's commissions had temporarily ceased, her mother established a shop in Islington, where lace, children's dresses, and fancy goods were sold. But Kate continued throughout her childhood to visit family and friends at Rolleston. Years later she was to write of the delights of this period. ' "The Fryers" garden was my loved one of all the gardens I have ever known,' she jotted down (and that was saying a good deal, for it would be hard to find anywhere a greater lover of gardens than she was). It was her real Paradise.

Round the windows of the Neales' house where Kate stayed, grew the biggest and brightest convolvuluses in the world (at least in the world she knew)—deep blue blossoms with 'pinky' stripes and deep pink blossoms with white stripes. Her intimacy with them told her every day where the newest blooms were to be found. Across the gravel path on the left as you emerged from 'The House' was a large oval bed, with roses, pinks, stocks, sweet Sultans, the brown scabious, white lilies, red

Mrs. Neale

25

lilies, red fuchsias, and in early summer, monster tulips, double white narcissus, peonies, crown imperials, and wallflowers. Indeed, all lovely flowers seemed to grow there. And the scent of them was a haunting memory through life. Then there were the biggest, thickest, and bushiest of box borders, nearly a yard high, so thick and solid that you could sit on them and they never gave way. These bounded the long gravel walk which led straight down to the bottom of the garden, and along which grew flowers of every lovely shape and hue. Beyond them on the left was the orchard—apples, pears, plums, and bushy filberts; on the right the kitchen garden—currant bushes with their shining transparent bunches, red and white, gooseberries, strawberries, feathery asparagus, and scented herbs such as good cooks and housewives love. There, too, there were birds innumerable—peacocks strutting and spreading their tails, guinea-fowls, turkeys with alarming voices and not less alarming ways, geese, pigeons, ducks, and fowls. It was an enchanted fairyland

The kitchen at Rolleston, an early watercolour by Kate Greenaway

to the little Londoner and had a far-reaching influence on her life and work. Later on her letters teemed with just such catalogues of flowers. So great was her love for them that, next to seeing them, the mere writing down of their names yielded the most pleasurable emotions.

When Kate was between five and six years old the family moved to a larger house and shop nearer to Highbury; here was the home of her recollection when she looked back on her childhood. And it was here that a new world opened to her, unfenced about with material walls, illimitable, inexhaustible—the world of books and measureless imagination. Her early wonder and sense of excitement at *Bluebeard, Beauty and the Beast, The Three Bears* and many other fairy stories and nursery rhymes were to remain with her throughout her life.

Of all her relations visited during these early years, Kate Greenaway loved best her mother's mother 'Grandma Jones.' She was a bright, clever, old lady, with a sharp tongue, fond of shrewd sayings and full of interesting information. Not her least charm was that she always had Coburg loaves for tea, beautiful toast, raspberry jam, and honey. Other relations of whom the little Greenaways saw a great deal were their aunts; Rebecca, a bookbinder; and Mary, a wood-engraver. Aunt Mary was a great favorite because she always had bread and treacle, or bread and butter and sugar, for tea.

Kate's devotion to her father doubtless had far-reaching results, for not only was he an accomplished engraver, but an artist of no mean ability. And there was a fascination and mystery about his calling which made a strong appeal to her imagination. As long as Kate could remember, her father's office was at 4, Wine Office Court, Fleet Street. There most of his work was done, but when, as frequently happened, there was a scramble to get the wood blocks engraved in time for the press, he would have to work the greater part of two consecutive nights. Then he would bring portions of his blocks home. These were times of superlative pleasure to Kate.

Among the many distractions of Kate's early years were her dolls, which ranged from the little giant 'Gauraca,' so huge—more than a 'ard and a quarter long—that she could only be carried with legs trailing along the ground, to the little group of Dutch mannikins. By right of bulk Gauraca claimed precedence. She wore the discarded clothes of Kate's brother John, born when Kate was six years old.

Below Gauraca came dolls of all sorts and sizes, too many for enumeration, but all of importance, seeing that on their persons were performed those tentative experiments which were to colour the work of twenty years later. Least in size though first in rank came the Royal group, with Queen Victoria (who had cost a halfpenny) as its centre, supported by Prince Albert (also a halfpenny).

It was in Islington that Kate had her first taste of systematic education, from Mrs. Allaman, who kept an infants' school—an old lady with a large frilly cap, a frilly muslin dress, a scarf over her shoulders, and a long apron. Here she learned her letters and how to use needle and cotton (put to such good effect in the clothing of her dolls and later models). On the whole she liked the old lady, but all her life long she could feel the sounding tap of her admonitory thimble on her infant head.

Her further education in this early period was unsatisfactory, although varied.

Several schools were tried, but Kate often became ill. So her education continued at home, where a lady came two or three times a week to give her lessons in French and music. After a few years Kate returned to the Misses Fiveash, with whom she remained until she left school altogether.

During this time the whole of Great Britain was stirred to its depths by the terrible events taking place in India. People talked and thought of little else besides the 1857 Mutiny, and the papers, prominent among them the *Illustrated London News*, played up to the public's hunger for literary and pictorial details. Many of the latter passed through the hands of Mr. Greenaway, and here is Kate's memorandum on the subject, written on an isolated leaf of her autobiographical notes: 'At the time of the Indian Mutiny I was always drawing people escaping. I could sit and think of the sepoys till I could be wild with terror, and

28

I used sometimes to dream of them. But I was always drawing the ladies, nurses, and children escaping. Mine always escaped and were never taken.'

Kate's father and mother were not blind to their daughter's artistic promise, and they believed the first opportunity must be taken of giving it a chance for growth and development. By the time she was twelve years old her artistic education had begun. The first art class she attended was held at William Street, Clerkenwell, near Claremont Square, a school in connection with the Science and Art Department (later the Board of Education). Kate showed undoubted signs of ability and was soon promoted to Miss Springet's school at Canonbury House, and here she remained. Her first prize was gained when she was only twelve, and it was determined that she should make Art her profession. She then enrolled in the chief school of the Art Department, under R. Burchett. In 1861 she was awarded the bronze medal; in 1864 the "National" for her drawing of tile designs; and in 1869 the silver (South Kensington).

The set of six tiles, here reproduced, display charming harmonies of colour. One is composed of olive-green and two different yellows on a slate-blue ground, while the flowers are outlined with white edges. In another, crimson-purple, russet-yellow, and blue are on a slate-grey ground; and in a third the grey-blue flowers are outlined with white, and

"The Picnic," an early pen and ink drawing

Set of tile drawings in colour, done by Kate Greenaway at the age of 17

grey-green, violet, purple, and yellow tell richly on a brown ground. The other schemes of colour are equally well combined, and the pattern designs are all good, and display a sense of grace and ability in line and arrangement. In addition to the awards mentioned, Kate received many book prizes in lieu of medals to which she was later entitled. Here she worked for several years with great diligence and thoroughness, undaunted by difficulties and hardships such as fall to the lot of few students. Indeed, so eagerly industrious was she that at the same time she attended the Life Classes at Heatherley's, and later on the newly opened London Slade School, then in charge of Professor Legros and his assistants.

In 1868, when Kate was twenty-two years old, her work made its first public appearance at the Dudley Gallery (Egyptian Hall, Piccadilly), when she exhibited a water-colour drawing entitled "Kilmeny," illustrating a versified legend, and "six little drawings on wood." Then there came a series of small pictures in water-colour at the same gallery, in which she already gave evidence of the bent which her brush was to follow with such remarkable success. Even then her fancy was leading

her back to the quaintly picturesque costume which was in vogue at the
close of the eighteenth century. Not that her enthusiasm for our grand-
mothers' gowns at once tickled the fancy of the public. That was to
come. Indeed, she herself was as yet only feeling her way, though with
remarkable deliberation and thoroughness. No doubt it was in her first
remunerative but anonymous work of designing valentines and Christmas cards that the possibilities which lay in childhood archaically, or
at least quaintly, attired first presented themselves to her, but the goal
was not to be reached without unstinted labour and active forethought.
Her subsequent success rested upon the thoroughness with which she
laid her foundations. She did not merely pick up an old book of
costumes and copy and adapt them second-hand to her own uses. She
began from the very beginning, fashioning the dresses with her own
hands and dressing up her models and lay-figures in order to realise the
effects anew. She would not allow herself any satisfaction until her
models lived and moved in her presence as their parents or grandparents
had lived and moved in the previous century. Only then was she sure
of her ground and could go forward with confidence.

Pencil and tint drawing

At the age of 21

At that early exhibition in 1868 Kate's work caught the eye of an excellent judge and a discriminating editor, the Rev. W. J. Loftie. He was much pleased with a frame of six drawings on wood, of sprites, gnomes, and fairies and also pictures of child life, and he secured them at once for use in *People's Magazine*, of which he was editor. Although work had already come to Kate through her father's instrumentality, the Rev. Loftie was her first outside employer. Eventually he wrote to Kate, and she visited him at his office. According to him, she was at this time very small, and seemed clever and sensible, with a certain impressive expression in her dark eyes that struck every one.

Although *People's Magazine* soon came to an end, Miss Greenaway was an artist who never disappointed her employers, and before long many opportunities occurred for recommending her. She had some work to do for Kronheim & Co. (a great colour-printing establishment in Shoe Lane) about that time, but—forgetting, apparently, her excellent achievement at South Kensington—she found a difficulty with colours. Like many beginners, she imagined that a sufficient number of bright colours made a bright-coloured picture, and being disappointed with the result, complained to the Rev. Loftie who got the little manual of Colour-Harmony which was prepared by Redgrave for the South Kensington authorities and gave it to her. In the meanwhile Messrs. Marcus Ward of Belfast had consulted the Rev. Loftie as to extending their business, and proposed to carry out a scheme he had laid before them some time before for issuing artistic Christmas cards and valentines in gold and colours. Kate Greenaway entered into the idea with great zest, but at first her designs were, as she said herself, gaudy. A little study of colour-harmony soon showed her where the fault lay, and she used to ask her friend to set her exercises in it—in primaries, or secondaries, or tertiaries, as the case might be. She derived extraordinary pleasure from studying the colour scale of such a picture as Van Eyck's 'Jean Arnolfini and his Wife' in the National Gallery, or Gainsborough's so-called 'Blue Boy.' It was only by incessant study of this kind earnestly pursued that she acquired the delicate and exquisite facility for figures and flowers in colour by which she soon became known. Meanwhile she drew constantly in black and white, and illustrated a child's book, *Topo*, by Miss Blood, afterwards Lady Colin Campbell, which was published by Messrs. Ward and speedily went out of print. A volume of valentines, *The Quiver of Love*, was published about the same time, and contained

32

Early sketch for a
Christmas card

specimens of colour-printing by the same firm after her drawings and those of Mr. Walter Crane.

Kate Greenaway worked very hard at the production of the designs for birthday cards and valentines. They constantly improved in harmony of colour and delicacy of effect.

Her first great success was a valentine. It was designed for Messrs. Marcus Ward of Belfast, whose London manager hardly recognised, in the Rev. Loftie's opinion, what a prize they had found. The rough proof of the drawing, in gold and colour, is both crude and inharmonious, but it has merits of delicacy and composition which account for the fact that the firm is said to have sold upwards of 25,000 copies of it in a few weeks. Her share of the profits was probably no more than £3. She painted many more on the same terms that year and the next, and was constantly improving in every way as she became better acquainted with her own powers and with the capabilities, at that time very slight, of printing in colour.

Study from life.
An illustration by Kate Greenaway
for *Ronald's Clock*
by Mrs. M. S. Spielmann

As soon as the introduction by the Rev. Loftie to Messrs. Marcus Ward was brought about, Kate Greenaway made a practice of consulting William Marcus Ward on the subject of her artistic and literary ambitions. In the matter of her drawing and painting she bowed to his expert opinion, unhesitatingly destroying her work when he told her that it was bad, and for years profited by his kindly advice; but when in the matter of her verses he told her that her efforts were 'rubbish and without any poetic feeling,' though she listened meekly enough, she reserved her opinion—as we shall see in the event, not without some measure of justification.

After working for the firm for six or seven years, during which time her designs were trump cards in their annual pack, she was advised by friends that the drawings ought to be returned to her after reproduction. This new departure, however, did not meet with her employers' approval, and the connection ceased.

'I have a beautiful design,' says the Rev. Loftie, 'in the most delicate tints, for another valentine, which she brought me herself to show how much better she now understood harmony. It was unfinished, and in fact was never used by the firm. I need not go into the circumstances under which she severed her connection with them, but I well remember her remarkable good-temper and moderation. In the end it was for her benefit. Edmund Evans seized the chance, and eventually formed the partnership which subsisted for many years, till near the end of her life.'

Kate was always very humble about herself, according to the Rev. Loftie. She was the very last person to recognise her own eminence, and was always, to the very end, keen to find out if any one could teach her anything or give her a hint or a valuable criticism. She was also very shy in general society, and inclined to be silent and to keep in the background.

Up to the year 1871 it is not possible to be very precise as to Kate's progress towards the overwhelming popularity which she was so soon to win. But from that time onwards her systematic keeping of accounts enables us to be definite. Besides the work done for Kronheim, for which she was paid £36, we have the entry, 'Happy Wretched Family,' 10s.; 'Tracts' (apparently for the Religious Tract Society), £2:5s.; and commissions for a Mr. Sheers and Mr. Griffith, £24:10s.; the year's takings amounting to something over £70.

The preceding year she had been represented at the Dudley Gallery by a water-colour drawing entitled 'Apple-Blossom—A Spring Idyll'; and in

Suffolk Street, for the first time, by another entitled 'A Peeper,' representing children at play. In 1871 too, as we know from the Rev. Loftie, she was designing Christmas cards for Marcus Ward of Belfast. In these drawings she adopted the style of dress which she had seen as a child about the farm at Rolleston, where there was a survival of costumes which had long since disappeared from the towns and more 'progressive' villages and country districts, adapting them to her purpose and filling her wardrobes with frocks, bonnets, and jackets and other garments, partly conjured up from memory and partly invented. She soon began to discover that she was creating a vogue. She felt their quaintness and charm herself, and was hardly surprised that others found them equally attractive. And notwithstanding some doubts thrown by her father, artist though he was, upon her wisdom in proceeding upon these lines, she determined to persist, and events proved her instinct to be right. Fortunately, her friend Stacy Marks, R. A., at the moment of crisis, gave her strong support, and in the face of universal opposition urged her to continue in the path on which she had entered.

In 1872 she was designing yellow-back covers for Edmund Evans, of whom much will be heard later. At the same time she was doing work for Kronheim, she found her way into the *Illustrated London News*, and she sold her pictures at the Dudley Gallery for something like £20.

By 1873, doubtless through the influence of her father, who at that time was doing much work for Cassell, Petter, & Galpin, Kate made her first appearance in *Little Folks*, for which, as well as for other publica-

tions of the firm, she executed innumerable dainty and characteristic drawings. This, of course, was mostly journeyman's work, and she was hampered by having to express other people's ideas pictorially. She never excelled as an illustrator, and it was not till she had a free hand that she did herself full justice. It was, however, an excellent school wherein to test her powers and to gain the experience which led her eventually to 'find herself.' In many of these wood-engravings it is interesting to notice the joint signature 'K. Greenaway, del.,' and 'J. Greenaway, sc.' She disliked being bound by another person's imagination, and her aversion to 'mere illustration' remained with her to the end.

Kate was now a person of some importance in the Greenaway establishment. Not only had she adopted a profession, but she was making that profession pay, and the time was coming when she felt that there should be some tangible sign, at least so far as she was concerned, of the improvement in their fortunes. It was a cause of profound gratification to her mother, who, by dint of thrift and self-sacrifice and devotion amounting almost to heroism, had been enabled to realise her ambition to educate each of her children to the greatest advantage. Her eldest daughter was sent to the Royal Academy of Music; her son to the Royal College of Chemistry; and Kate to South Kensington and Heatherley's. All of them were on the high-road to success, and a sense of satisfaction and good-humour permeated the household.

Good-humour, indeed, was characteristic of Kate, and to this sweetness of disposition and thoughtfulness for others she owed not a little of her success. Artist's grown-up models are often difficult enough to manage, but child-models are apt to prove exasperating; and it was due only to her infinite tact and unwearing resourcefulness in inventing amusements and distractions for her little sitters that she coaxed them into good temper and into displaying the charm which she was so successful in reproducing.

During the last year or two spent in Islington, Kate rented near by a room which she fitted up as a studio, but about 1873 or 1874 she and her father between them bought the lease of a house in Pemberton Gardens, where the family lived till 1885.

Her friend Mrs. Miller writes of her at this period: 'She was then as ever gentle, patient, industrious, exquisitely sensitive, extraordinarily humorous, while under and over it all was an indomitable will. I always remember one little remark she made to me once when we were walking from her home in Islington to a little room she had taken as a studio (her first) in a side street. It was wet and miserable, the streets vulgar and sordid. "Never mind," she said, "I shall soon be in the spring." The first primrose she drew upon the sheet before her would place her in another world. She loved all sorts of street music, and once said to me, "The moment I hear a band, I am in fairyland." '

In 1874 Kate illustrated a little volume of fairy stories entitled *Fairy Gifts or A Wallet of Wonders*, and written by Kathleen Knox. This was the first time Kate's name appeared on a title page.

Up until now Kate had been going through the usual experiences of the free-lance who with pen or pencil in hand sets forth to win recognition from the public. By 1877, when she took her studio to College Place, Liverpool Road, Islington, her earnings had nearly reached £300. Although fairly prosperous, therefore, she could scarcely consider herself successful. This was the first year in which she appeared in the Royal Academy Exhibition, and sold her picture, Musings, for twenty guineas. She was a recognized contributor to the Dudley Gallery and was pretty sure of buyers there. She was getting more or less regular employment on the *Illustrated London News*, and she had been asked by W. L. Thomas, editor of the newly established *Graphic*, to provide him with a running pictorial full-page story. Nevertheless, in her own opinion, she was but a successful artist-hack. All this was to be changed by a business arrangement, almost amounting to a partnership, in which she was to take her full share of the credit as well as of the spoil.

Edmund Evans, with whom this new arrangement was made, was then primarily a colour-printer; his wood-engraving department was subsidiary. For the purposes of his business he owned a good many machines; he had three houses all of them in the City, and he was sometimes puzzled to find work to keep them going, to do which is at the root of commercial economy and success in his business. He printed most of the 'yellow-backs' of the time, covers for books as well as for small magazines of a semi-religious character, working-men's magazines, and so forth, all with much colour-work in them. Evans also executed much high-class work of the kind, such as Doyle's *Chronicles of England*, which had done much to make his reputation. Therefore, to fill up the spare time during which his machines would otherwise be idle, he began publishing

the toy-books of Walter Crane, then those of Randolph Caldecott, and finally he turned his attention to Kate Greenaway.

It should be recorded to the credit of Edmund Evans that he excelled all others in the skill with which he produced his colour-effects with a small number of printings. John Greenaway, Kate's father, himself an expert in the preparation of blocks for colour-printing, as well as an artist of much intelligence, used to declare that no other firm in London could come near the result that Edmund Evans would get with as few, say, as three colour-blocks, so wonderful was his ingenuity, so great his artistic taste, and so accurate his eye.

Evans informs us:

I had known John Greenaway, father of K. G., as Kate Greenaway was known to most of her friends and relations, since I was fourteen years of age. He was an assistant engraver to Ebenezer Landells, originator of *Punch*, to whom I was apprenticed. I knew he was having one of his daughters educated for the musical profession and another for drawing. I had only seen engravings made from drawings on wood by 'K. G.' for Cassell & Co., as well as some Christmas cards by Marcus Ward & Co. from water-colour drawings of very quaint little figures of children. Very beautiful they were, for they were beautifully lithographed.

About 1877-78 K. G. came to see us at Witley, bringing a collection of about fifty drawings she had made, with quaint verses written to them. I was fascinated with the originality of the drawings and the ideas of the verse, so I at once purchased them and determined to reproduce them in a little volume. The title *Under the Window* was selected afterwards from one of the first lines. At the suggestion of George Routledge & Sons I took the drawings and verses to Frederick Locker, the author of *London Lyrics*, to 'look over' the verses, not to rewrite them, but only to correct a few oddities which George Routledge & Sons did not quite like or understand. Locker was very much taken with the drawings and the verses, and showed them to Mrs. Locker with quite a gusto; he asked me many questions about her, and was evidently interested in what I told him of her. I do not think that he did anything to improve the verses, nor did K. G. herself.

Locker soon made her acquaintance and introduced her into some very good society. She often stayed stayed with them at Rowfant, Sussex, and also at Cromer.

George Eliot was at the time staying at Witley. She called on us one day and saw the drawings and was much charmed with them. A little time afterwards I wrote to George Eliot to ask if she would write me a

38

short story of, or about, children suitable for K. G. to illustrate. Her reason for refusing was interesting:—

> 'THE HEIGHTS, WITLEY,
> *October* 22, 1879.

'Dear Mr. Evans—It is not my way to write anything except from my own inward prompting. Your proposal does me honour, and I should feel much trust in the charming pencil of Miss Greenaway, but I could never say "I will write this or that" until I had myself felt the need to do it. . . .—Believe me, dear Mr. Evans, yours most sincerely,

> M. E. LEWES.'

After I had engraved the blocks and colour-blocks, I printed the first edition of 20,000 copies, and was ridiculed by the publishers for risking such a large edition of a six-shilling book; but the edition sold before I could reprint another edition ; in the meantime copies were sold at a premium. Reprinting kept on till 70,000 was reached.

I volunteered to give K. G. one-third of the profit of this book. It was published in the autumn of 1878. We decided to publish *The Birthday Book for Children* in 1880. Miss Greenaway considered that she should have half the profits of all books we might do together in future, and that I should return to her the original drawings after I had paid her for them and reproduced them. To both these terms I willingly agreed. However, the half-share royalty only became payable after the expenses of publication had been cleared off—that is to say, after the sale had passed a given number of copies. Consequently, as certain of the books never reached the limit, K. G. only received payment for the use of the drawings, which were returned to her. Such failures, commercially speaking, were *A Day in a Child's Life*, the Calendars, and one or two more. It was found in practice that, except in rare cases, books with music were not successful.

Then came the *Birthday Book, Mother Goose,* and part of *A Day in Child's Life'* in 1881; *Little Ann*, 1883; the *Language of Flowers, Kate Greenaway's Painting-Book,* and *Mavor's Spelling-Book*, 1884-85; *Marigold Garden* 1885; *A Apple Pie* and *The Queen of The Pirate Isle* 1886; *The Pied Piper of Hamelin*, 1888; *The Book of Games* and *King Pepito*, 1889. Besides the above and a certain number of smaller issues, minor works, and detached designs, the artist was responsible for an Almanack from 1883 to 1897, with the sole exception of the year 1896.

The books named above are those which we did together.

Of *Under the Window*, which was published at the end of 1878, it is no exaggeration to say that it was epoch-making; its popularity was such that Kate tasted the bitter-sweet experience of finding her work coolly appropriated by others.

There are, however, one or two facts connected with the book which demand attention. In the first place, from this moment Kate Greenaway's name became a household word, not only in Great Britain, but in a vast number of homes on the continents of Europe and America. In the second place, for the first time she was not hampered in her published work by adapting her fancy to the literary ideas of other people, but was inspired by subjects which came red-hot from the furnace of her own imagination.

This is a matter of no little importance. It is clear that the ideal illustrator of a literary idea, if only the technical skill is not wanting, is the person to whose mind that idea first presents itself. The writer alone knows exactly what he means and what he wants. His pencil may be unskilled, but it is nerved by the original thought. It is because Thackeray had the double gift that his drawings, although so weak in execution, yet so evidently imbued with the living literary inspiration, so greatly commend themselves to those who look for genuine sincerity of inspiration, and not only for beauty of composition and execution. That is why the world revelled in du Maurier's *Peter Ibbetson* and *Trilby*, and why Blake's *Songs of Innocence and Experience* is one of the completest and most harmonious books in existence.

What Blake did, Kate Greenaway was now enabled to do, in her own fashion, in *Under the Window*. She was expressing her own literary thoughts and at the same time treating them pictorially.

When the original drawings for *Under the Window* were exhibited at the Fine Art Society two years later, the critics vied with one another in their applause. Ruskin in particular exhausted the splendour of his vocabulary in his praise of their unaffected beauty, their sweetness and naïveté, their delicacy of sentiment, subtlety of humour, and the exquisiteness of technique.

Wherefore it is evident that the success was as deserved as it was instantaneous. Nor was it due only to the fortunate moment chosen for launching the book. There was at least one other felicitous circumstance: Miss Greenaway was exceptionally fortunate in her interpreter, who had brought colour-printing by means of wood blocks to a pitch of excellence never before attempted.

In 1878, the year that produced *Under the Window*, also saw the publication of *Topo, or Summer Life in Italy*, by Gertrude Blood (afterwards Lady Colin Campbell) 'with 44 pen-and-ink illustrations by Kate Greenaway.'

For these illustrations, William Marcus Ward, the book's publisher, tells us, Kate Greenaway made innumerable sketches—was indeed tireless in her determination to do the best for her text. These preliminary designs were thrown off with amazing rapidity, 'almost as quickly as they could be talked about.' Those rejected she would ruthlessly tear up or beg him to do so. For the donkey she made at least a dozen drawings, but with no success, and finally had to submit to the mortification of the animal being drawn by some one else.

Randolph Caldecott, born the same year as Kate Greenaway, was not only her rival and competitor, but her admiring friend and helpful comrade. In a letter to her dated September 30, 1878, he advises her in this way:

'The brown ink of which I discoursed will not, when thickly used with a pen, keep itself entirely together under the overwhelming influence of a

Kate Greenaway in 1880

brush with water-colour. I have found this out today. But the liquid Indian ink used for lines will stand any number of damp assaults. This I know from much experience.—Believe me, yours very truly,   R. Caldecott.
P.S.—I hope the above information may be of use to you.—R.C.

On the other hand, with Walter Crane—with whose name her own was so often linked in the public mind, as well as in publishers' announcements—Kate Greenaway had but the slightest acquaintance, though for his work she entertained unbounded admiration. Crane informs us:

I only met her on one occasion, and that was at a play given in Argyll Street, wherein Tennyson's second son, Lionel Tennyson, appeared, and in which the Lockers were interested.

My impressions of Kate Greenaway were of a very quiet and unobtrusive personality, probably quietly observant, self-contained, reserved, with a certain shrewdness. She was small and plainly dressed.

In those days it was usual to bracket Kate Greenaway, Randolph Caldecott, and myself together as special children's-book providers, ignoring very great differences of style and aims (ignoring, too, the fact that I began my series of picture-books more than ten years before either Caldecott or Miss Greenaway were known to the public). Both those artists, however, were, I fancy, much more commercially successful than I was, when I began, children's-book designs were very poorly paid. I was glad to be of some service to Caldecott when he started his series through Messrs. Routledge in 1878. My *Baby's Opera* was published in 1877 by the same house, and proved so successful that the publishers wanted me to follow it up immediately with another. Being engaged in other work, I did not see my way to this; but the publishers were equal to the emergency, for I was rather startled about Christmas to see Kate Greenaway's first book, *Under the Window*, announced by them as 'companion volume' to *The Baby's Opera*. To this I naturally objected as misleading, and the advertisement was withdrawn.

The grace and charm of her children and young girls were quickly recognised, and her treatment of quaint early nineteenth-century costume, prim gardens, and the child-like spirit of her designs in an old-world atmosphere, though touched with conscious modern 'æstheticism,' captivated the public in a remarkable way.

May I confess that (for me at least) I think she overdid the big bonnet rather, and at one time her little people were almost lost in their clothes? However, one saw this in the actual life of the day.

I remember Miss Greenaway used to exhibit drawings at the old Dudley

42

Gallery general exhibition, but her larger, more elaborated studies were not so happy as her book designs in simple outline tastefully tinted.

In 1878 Kate was represented at the Academy by her 'Little Girl with Doll,' while two of her pictures at the Dudley Gallery sold for fifteen guineas and fifteen pounds respectively, her gross takings from this source being nearly fifty pounds. Now, too, began her connection with the Scribners, for whom she worked for several years. From this time forward her accounts, to those who enjoy figures, make very cheerful reading. In 1878 she earned nearly £550, in 1879 over £800, in 1880 rather more, and in 1881 over £1500, the enormous rise being due to the accumulating royalties on the books engraved and printed by Mr. Evans and published by George Routledge & Sons.

The year 1846—the birth-year of both Kate Greenaway and Randolph Caldecott—marked also the genesis of the Christmas card. What was in the first instance a pretty thought and dainty whim, by its twenty-fifth year had become a craze . . .

Kate Greenaway had begun the designing of Christmas cards anonymously in the pre-collector days, and her earliest productions, which were no doubt an advance upon most of those which preceded them, are nevertheless interesting rather as curiosities than as works of art. In her valentines she had adopted the slashed doublet and buskin convention; but the Christmas card was to prove her triumph. Not that she shook herself free from her trammels all at once; but signs of grace quickly appeared, and the year 1878 found her working on original lines in the front rank of the artists who were taking advantage of the new departure. Before this date her cards seem never to have been signed, and are not

A Christmas greeting
for John Ruskin, 1890

easy to identify, as they lack the distinctive characteristics of her later work. As time goes on they bear, if not the initials 'K. G.,' at any rate the unquestionable evidence of her style. Doubtless the difficulty of identifying her early work is due chiefly to the fact that the designs, mainly flower pieces, were only sketched out by her and were given into the hands of more experienced draughtsmen to be finished. What was most noticeable in her work at this period was the remarkable ease with which she adapted her designs to the spaces they were to occupy, whether oblongs, uprights, circles, or ovals.

By this year she was, as *Under the Window* proves, in her own way 'drawing her inspiration from classic forms unfettered by classic conventions,' and her very original designs, coming at a time when the vogue was at its height, went no little way toward increasing her popularity.

But this section of her work, important though it was in her early development, was merely a by-path in the direction she was travelling. She was now, in truth, on the high-road to fame and success.

The next year, 1879, she was hard at work on her *Birthday Book*, with verses by Mrs. Sale Barker. It was published in 1880, and 128,000 English, 13,500 French, and 8,500 German copies were placed on the market. For the 382 tiny drawings, 370 of which were minute uncoloured figures, she received £151.10s, while the royalties eventually exceeded £1,100. It was this *Birthday Book* that prompted Robert Louis Stevenson to try his hand at those charming verses for children which were afterwards published in the *Child's Garden of Verse*.

In this year also Kate Greenaway was commissioned by Macmillan & Co. to illustrate a new edition of Miss Yonge's novels. But after finishing four drawings for the *Heir of Redclyffe* and three for *Heartsease*, she threw up the task.

The drawing called 'Misses,' which Kate sent this year to the Royal Academy, was less attractive to some than its foregoers. *Fun* fixed upon its title in a critical couplet:

> 'A picture by Miss Greenaway (we scarcely like a bit of it)
> Is rightly titled 'Misses,' for she hasn't made a hit of it!

The popular interest in Kate Greenaway then and thenceforward may be partly gauged by the great sheaf of applications for biographical information and addressed to her by the editors of various magazines, found among her papers.

Publishers too vied with one another in seeking her services, and a bare list of commissions offered but not taken in the years immediately succeeding would fill the pages of this book.

By 1880 Kate Greenaway began fully to realize the value of her drawings done for publication, and henceforward made it an inflexible rule to retain the drawings themselves and sell only the *use* of them.

By far the most important occurrence during the first part of 1880 was the beginning of her personal acquaintance with Frederick Locker, better known today as Frederick Locker-Lampson. He had heard of her from Edmund Evans two years earlier in connection with her verses for *Under the Window*, and many of Kate's happiest hours were spent in his company. Through him she seems to have become acquainted with Browning and his sister in 1882 and with the Tennyson family.

This year was also notable for what must have been a red-letter day in her life. Now for the first time Kate appeared in *Punch*, in an important drawing entitled 'Christmas is Coming' made by the masterly pencil of Linley Sambourne. Kate Greenaway heralded the preparations for this drawing in a letter to Locker-Lampson 'I heard again in a hurry from Linley Sambourne, and had to rush off yesterday and get a photo taken. So what I shall turn out like I dare not think, even if he could use it at all. I am curious to see what is going to be made of us all—if we are going to have large heads and little bodies, or how we are going to be made funny . . .'

In Mr. Sambourne's drawing, Mr. Punch, 'at home,' is invaded by a flight and crowd of artists, writers, and publishers of children's books— by Kate Greenaway, Caldecott, Stacy Marks, Mr. Harrison Weir, Mr.

Bookplate designed
for Frederick Locker
(F. Locker-Lampson)

Crane, and Mrs. Sale Barker, by Messrs. Macmillan, William Marcus Ward, Bradbury, Edmund Routledge, De la Rue, Hildesheimer, Duffield, and Walker, all caterers for the little ones, 'for all children,' says *Punch*, in the accompanying text, 'are Mr. Punch's pets. Let's see what you've got,' and forthwith he gives the place of honour to Miss Kate Greenaway, and warmly congratulates her on her *Birthday Book for Children*, 'a most dainty little work and a really happy thought for Christmas.' And a mother and her children are shown listening behind the door to Mr. Punch's declaration.

This was in itself a gratifying evidence of Kate Greenaway's popularity, but that it did not give much satisfaction to her friends is demonstrated by a letter from Mary Anderson, who wrote, 'Thank you so much for sending me the *Punch*. I had the greatest difficulty in finding your portrait. What a horror! It is actionable really!' The fact is, the photograph from which the sketch was made was unflattering in the extreme.

'K. G.' was destined several times to engage *Punch's* attention, but it may safely be said that no press notice ever gave her greater pleasure than that which attended her first appearance in his pages.

H. Stacy Marks, R. A., was one of Kate Greenaway's most valued and helpful friends. A constant visitor and advisor, and an ardent admirer of her work from early days, he did more than anyone to encourage her, to foster her genius, and to bring her into notice. His letters to her show how sincere and kind he was, and how candid a critic. It is through his correspondence with K. G. that we first learn of her introduction to John Ruskin, whose friendship was to become the outstanding feature of her life apart from her painting. Ruskin took the art of Kate Greenaway very seriously long before she became personally known to him. We learn of his hesitation in opening a correspondence with her through a fragment of a letter in all probability addressed to their common friend Stacy Marks:

It is a feeling of the same kind which keeps me from writing to Miss Greenaway–the oftener I look at her designs, the more I want a true and deep tone of colour,–and a harmony which should distinctly represent either sunshine, or shade, or true local colour.—I do not know how far with black outline this can be done but I would fain see it attempted. And also I want her to make more serious use of her talent–and show the lovely things that *are, and* the terrible which *ought to be known* instead of mere ugly nonsense, like that brown witch. (The lurid and dramatic witch in *Under the Window*.)—If she would only do what she naturally feels, and

would wish to teach others to feel without any reference to saleableness–
she probably would do lovelier things than any one could tell her–and I
could not tell her rightly I knew something of her own mind, even what
might be immediately suggestive to her, unless perhaps harmfully. Please
tell me your own feeling about her things.   J.R.

Stacy Marks wrote to Kate Greenaway in a letter dater November 3,
1879:

> . . . Mr. Ruskin dined here on Thursday last, and spoke in high terms of
> your feeling for children, etc. I think it not unlikely that you may have a
> letter from him soon.

And sure enough before three months were out Ruskin did make
it his business to write and give her shrewd and humorous advice. The
first letter is dated 1879, but that which follows shows this is a mistake:
like a great many other people, he found it hard to adopt a new date at
the beginning of a new year. Ruskin and Kate Greenaway, whose friendship was soon to ripen into a happy intimacy, shared by his household,
did not meet face to face until 1882.

A correspondence, however, ensued, which led up, on December 29,
1882, to this laconic but all-important entry in her diary: 'Mr. Ruskin
came. First time I ever saw him.' Concerning this interesting first meeting Mrs. Arthur Severn, Ruskin's cousin and adopted daughter, writes:
'I shall never forget this rapturous delight in first making her acquaintance.'

From the first moment of their meeting a friendship sprang up which
grew in strength and mutual appreciation until his death in 1900. Not
only did they constantly meet either in her house at Hampstead or at
Brantwood, where she paid him several delightful visits, but they carried
on a spirited correspondence, which on his side certainly ran to five
hundred letters, and on hers to probably double that number (Examples
of their letters on p. 68). When, in 1888, illness compelled him to cease
writing, Kate made it her kindly business to continue her frequent
missives in order to add to the pleasures and relieve the monotony of
a comparatively inactive old age. And in order to amuse and delight him,
she illustrated nearly every letter with one sketch at least.

In 1881 Routledge & Sons published *Mother Goose or the Old
Nursery Rhymes*, Illustrated by Kate Greenaway—one of her daintiest
productions, although marred in several instances by crude printer's ink
and careless register. Its success, though not equalling that of the

On a letter to Ruskin

Birthday Book, was very great—66,000 copies being printed in English, German, and French. The sum of £252 was paid to her for the use of the drawings, and in royalties she received over £650. The books bears on the title page the baby thrown into a basket of roses which so took Ruskin's fancy that he spoke of it at length in his lecture on Kate Greenaway at Oxford. Mrs. Allingham, mutual friend and artist, also the subject of Ruskin's lecture, said: "No one could draw roses like Kate Greenaway," and other critics have compared her drawing of flowers with the work of Botticelli.

Punch turned his attention to Kate Greenaway on no fewer than three separate occasions in 1881, a year in which she worked on *A Day in a Child's Life*, with music by Myles B. Foster (to be published by Routledge & Sons). Commercially considered, this extremely pretty book was a success, 25,000 copies being issued to the English-speaking world alone—although the press was not unanimous in its approval.

The year 1882 was chiefly occupied with the illustrations for a new edition of that early love of Kate Greenaway's, *Little Ann and Other Poems* by Jane and Ann Taylor.

She was now suffering more than ever from imitators, particularly on the continent. In Belgium where she had a great vogue not only were her books themselves being imitated, but the illustrations were copied without acknowldgement on to handkerchiefs, plates, vases, caskets, and other objects of commerce. All this tended, as her friend Frederick Locker predicted, to vulgarise the Fairyland which she was creating. As far as she could, Kate combatted the evil by refusing to part with the copyright of her works.

The beginning of 1883 had seen the publication of Kate Greenaway's first *Almanack*. Published at one shilling by George Routledge & Sons, and of course engraved and printed in colours by Edmund Evans, it achieved an enormous success, some 90,000 copies being sold in England, America, France, and Germany. It was succeeded by an almanack every year (with but one exception, 1896) until 1897, the last being published by Dent. The illustrations were printed on sheets with blank spaces for the letterpress, in which English, French, or German was inserted as the market demanded. There are various little conceits about these charming productions which are calculated to appeal to the 'licquorish chapman of such wares'; so that complete sets of them already fetch respectable sums from the collectors of beautiful books,

On a letter to Ruskin

especially when they have not been divested of the paper envelopes or wrappers in which they were originally issued.

It has been said—let us admit, with a little exaggeration—that Kate Greenaway dressed the children of two continents. In such measure as it is true, this was mainly due to the fact that her almanacks found a regular sale in France, from which America and Europe so largely take their cue in feminine matters sartorial.

In the summer of 1883 a charming collaboration took place in the pages of the *Magazine of Art* (which was then under the editorship of W. E. Henley) between Kate Greenaway and a poet in whose tender, exquisite, and dainty art she took infinite delight—Austin Dobson. Earlier in the year an article in that magazine on 'Art in the Nursery' had paid homage to the work of Kate Greenaway, along with that of Walter Crane, Randolph Caldecott, Lizzie Lawson, and Ernest Griset. But Kate is the heroine of the band, and the 'peculiar quality of cherubic dowdiness' of her youngsters, the winsomeness of the babies' solemn flirtation under an immense umbrella, and similar fascinating scenes, received the appreciation that was their due. Then in a number of the magazine that contained contributions by Robert Louis Stevenson, Cosmo Monkhouse, Leader Scott, W. C. Brownell, and others, Kate Greenaway contributed her charming page-drawing in which Austin Dobson's equally delicious verses were set.

In 1883 Kate Greenaway worked on illustrations for Ruskin's *Fors Clavigera: Letters to the Workmen and Labourers of Great Britain*. One headpiece showed a charming little girl watching the sun set across the sea. This was followed by a sweet and dainty little dancing maiden as headpiece to Letter 93, headpiece and tailpiece to Letter 94, headpiece to Letter 95, and full-page frontispiece to Letter 96. In the last-named a dancing babe of fortune leads by the hand a still more fascinating babe in rags—the rags and babe as clean and sweet as are all the rags and babes in Kate Greenaway's child-Utopia, whilst a dainty lady tripping in the rear impartially scatters roses over them from a basket under her arm. Her drawings in no way illustrated the text but were wholly adventitious decorations. These are the only Kate Greenaway drawings published by Ruskin, saving those to *Dame Wiggins* (1885). The only one of the 'Letters' in which Kate Greenaway is referred to by name is No. 94, 'Retrospect.'

This was the year of Ruskin's lecture on 'Kate Greenaway and Mrs.

49

Allingham' in his series given to Oxford undergraduates on "The Art of England." (See p. 73).

In 1884 Kate published a new *Almanack*, with an enlarged format—an experiment that was not repeated. Her *Language of Flowers* was the most ambitious project of the year; an edition of 19,500 was printed, over half going to America. This book, like the *Almanack*, failed to please Ruskin, who wrote on October 8 with his usual directness:

'You are working at present wholly in vain. There is *no* joy and very, very little interest in any of these Flower book subjects, and they look as if you had nothing to paint them with but starch and camomile tea.'

The fact is that the book was printed on unsuitable paper and much effect was hereby lost. Still the illustrations include some of the most exquisitely drawn figures and flowers she ever produced.

Kate Greenaway sent a copy of *Language of Flowers* to Ruskin's cousin and adopted daughter Mrs. Arthur Severn, with the following note:

'I send you my little book. Mr. Ruskin thinks it very bad. He says he's ashamed to show it to anyone—I hope it won't affect you so fearfully. I am very disgusted myself—*only I don't* feel *I am* so much to blame as the printers who have literally blotted every picture out.'

Then came *Kate Greenaway's Painting-Book* which, although it consisted of blocks brought together from *Under the Window*, *Kate Greenaway's Birthday Book*, *A Day in a Child's Life*, *Marigold Garden*, and *Mother Goose*, had nevertheless a great and deserved success, and set at least forty thousand children painting away at her delightful designs.

This was followed by *Mavor's Spelling-Book*, surely, as now illustrated by K. G., one of the most inspiring school-books ever published for children, with the beautifully engraved cuts printed in brown in the text. Ruskin wrote of it: 'Spelling Book ever so nice—But do children really learn to spell like that? I never did.'

Only 5,000 copies of the book were called for. But when the publishers issued the capital letters alone in a tiny square volume entitled *Kate Greenaway's Alphabet*, the vagaries of book-buying were curiously exemplified by the fact that the circulation reached a total of 24,500 copies.

Marigold Garden, published in 1885, of which Kate Greenaway was once more both author and illustrator, added largely to the artist's re-

50

putation; sales were large, England taking 6,500, America 7,500, and France 3,500 copies.

In 1885 was also published *Dame Wiggins of Lee and Her Seven Wonderful Cats, a humorous tale written principally by a lady of ninety.* These nursery rhymes had first come out in 1823, but Ruskin added some verses of his own and some illustrations by Kate Greenaway. In the original edition were woodcuts coloured by hand. In the 1885 edition these were facsimiled in outline and left, as Ruskin says in the preface, 'for clever children . . . to colour in their own way.' Of his and Kate Greenaway's part in the republication he says: 'I have added the rhymes on the third, fourth, eighth and ninth pages—the kindness of Miss Greenaway supplying the needful illustrations. But my rhymes do not ring like the real ones; and I would not allow Miss Greenaway to subdue the grace of her first sketches to the formality of the earlier work.'

The warmest friendship and affection had by now developed between K. G. and Mrs. Arthur Severn. Perhaps the fact that K. G., to whom the love of children was as the very breath of her life, had no children of her own, made her particularly fond of the offspring of her friends. She not only painted them for their parents' delight, but amused them with her drawings and stories. For Mrs. Severn's little daughter Violet, K. G. composed the doleful history of a naughty girl, and we reproduce a facsimile of the original four-page story here.

On Monday, February 16, 1885, Miss Greenaway moved to Hampstead, into the house at 39, Frognal designed for her by Norman Shaw, her home until her death. Ruskin did not care for the new house. 'I am aghast at the house at Hampstead, and quite resolved that you *shan't* live in London. . . . I'll make your life a burden to you if you live in London!' Just before she moved, Ruskin wrote K. G.: 'You're not going to call your house a Villa!? Could you call it Kate's State—or Kitty's Green—or Katherine's Nest,—or Brownie's Cell—or Camomile Court— or Lassie's Leisure—or the Romp's Rest—or—something of that sort?' and again:

'I will take real care about the addresses—but I really must have a pretty one for the New House—you don't suppose I'm going to write Frognal every day of my life—it might as well be Dognal—Hognal— Lognal—I won't. If it is to be I'll have it printed!!!'

But Kate saved him the trouble, keeping him henceforth supplied

The house at 39, Frognal, Hampstead,
designed for Kate Greenaway
by R. Norman Shaw

with sheaves of envelopes addressed to herself in her own handwriting.

Even her friend Frederick Locker wasn't pleased with the house. K. G. wrote to Mrs. Severn on March 25: 'Mr. Locker came to see this new studio yesterday. He said, "What a frightful *falling off* from the *old one*." Isn't that sad?—but I fear true.'

But she was pleased to think that although it was not so pretty as her last studio, it was larger, lighter, and altogether more practical.

The household included Kate's father and mother and her brother, John Greenaway. Mr. Greenaway was still practising as a wood-engraver with an office in the city; John Greenaway was the sub-editor of the *Journal of the Chemical Society*. He writes of his sister's routine at Frognal during this time in her life:

52

Of my sister at work, we saw very little. She very wisely made it a fixed rule that, during working hours, no one should come into the studio save on matters of urgency. Her great working time was the morning, so she was always an early riser and finished breakfast by eight o'clock. Her most important work was done between then and luncheon time (1 o'clock). Practically she never went out in the morning. After luncheon she usually worked for an hour or two, unless she was going out anywhere for the afternoon; and then went for a walk on the Heath, and came back to tea. The evenings up to eight o'clock, when we had a meal that was a sort of compromise between dinner and supper, were spent in letter-writing, making dresses for models, occasionally working out schemes and rough sketches for projected books and such-like things; but all finished work was done in the morning or afternoon. In the summer too, a good deal of this time was spent in the garden seeing to her flowers. After supper she generally lay on a sofa and read until she went to bed at about 10 o'clock.

She could not stand late hours and seldom went out in the evening. For the same reason she very seldom dined out. Tea-time was always her time for going out to see friends, or for them to see her.

All in all, the change of abode was a great success.

During the summer of 1885 Ruskin fell seriously ill. In Kate's laconic diary we find the following unusually concise entries:

July 31.	He is much worse today.
August 11.	Still as ill.
August 13.	No change yet, still so quiet.
August 14.	Slightly better.
August 15.	Still better.
August 19.	Still better and downstairs.
August 24.	Still getting better but so slowly.
August 25.	Still better.
August 26.	First drive.
August 28.	Out in garden alone.

Early in 1886 Ruskin had recovered sufficiently to resume work on *Praeterita*, his autobiography, and occupied much of his leisure by working on drawings which he had made in early life. Beginning by sending them to Kate Greenaway for criticism, he ended by insisting on her keeping for herself one out of every ten, finding much amusement in guessing which would be her choice week by week. The whole thing was a pretty contest in generosity between the great critic and his devoted admirer.

53

Besides the *Almanack of 1886*, of which 45,000 copies were issued, Kate had a gratifying success with *A Apple Pie*, published by Routledge & Sons. Ruskin did not approve of it very much, but he did like the *The Queen of the Pirate Isle*, by Bret Harte, illustrated by Kate Greenaway with many charming coloured engravings, calling it "the best thing she had ever done." This came out actually in 1887, as did the new *Almanack*, of which over 37,000 copies were sold. She also may have designed a cover for *The Peace of Polissena*, by Miss Francesca Alexander, a part of *Christ's Folk in the Appennine*, edited and partly written by Ruskin, but it does not appear to have been used—perhaps as a result of the Master's illness of this year.

Facsimile of a four-page picture-story written and illustrated by Kate Greenaway for Violet Severn

THE . NAUGHTY . LITTLE
GIRL
WHO . WENT TO SEE HER
GRANDMAMA

Once there was a little girl. and one nice fine afternoon. Her mama said her nurse might take her to have tea with her Grandmamas — if the little girl would promise to be a very good little girl indeed for I'm sorry to tell you she was often a very bad little girl — indeed — and did all sorts of things she ought not to do. but she said she would be a very nice child indeed to day — so she had her

Beside the execution of private commissions, Kate Greenaway published the sixth *Almanack* in 1888. The same year Routledge & Sons published *The Pied Piper of Hamelin,* by Robert Browning, with 35 illustrations by Kate Greenaway and engraved and printed in colours by Edmund Evans. The book met with immediate and gratifying success, and Ruskin spoke of it as the 'grandest thing' Kate had ever done.

But the crowning event of the year was the friendship being formed with Mrs. Allingham (also the subject of Ruskin's Oxford lecture), with whom sixteen years before she had worked as a student at the Slade. Much later Mrs. Allingham wrote of her friend:

> It must have been in 1872 or 1873 that I first met Kate Greenaway at an evening class at the Slade School (which I only attended for three months). I had given up my student work at the R.A. schools—(she doubtless had then left Kensington) for drawing on the wood in my own studio.

I was not formally introduced to her till several years after I was married, when I met her at an evening party at Tennyson's—in Belgrave Square, I think. Mr. Frederick Locker presented me to her, and we had a pleasant talk, I remember. In 1881, we went to live at Witley in Surrey, and among our kindest neighbours were Mr. and Mrs. Edmund Evans, with whom Kate often came to stay.

For several years we (K. and I) had merely pleasant friendly meetings without in any way becoming intimate. I think it was in the spring of 1888 that we went out painting together in the copses near Witley and became really *friends*. In the autumn of that year we removed to Hampstead, and it was always a pleasure to visit Kate in her beautiful home and to sit and chat with her by the hour in her cosy little tea-room or in the great studio full of interesting things. When the time came for saying good-night, she would always come down to the hall-door and generally put on a hat hanging in the hall and come as far as the gate for more friendly last words.

In the spring of 1890 . . . she and I went out painting together daily, either to some of the pretty old thatched cottages around Farringford or to the old dairy in the grounds, when we often had a friendly visit from the great poet himself, or from Mr. Hallam Tennyson, with an invitation to come up to tea . . .

She was always scrupulously thoughtful for the convenience and feelings of the owners of the farm or cottage we wished to paint, with the consequence that *we* were made welcome to sit in the garden or orchard where *others* were refused admittance.

I am afraid that her short sight must have greatly added to the difficulty of out-door painting for her. I remember her exclaiming one day, 'What am I to do? When I look at the roof it is all a red blur—when I put on my spectacles I see every crack in the tiles . . .'

She was one of the most sensitive of creatures and I think she felt that it might be wiser for both of us to discontinue the practice of working from

Her Grandmother - never let her Play in the Garden again and I think it served her right dont you — the Pussy was never made to run so fast any more - but sat in the Sun and enjoyed itself all day long - The Kind Grandmama - had nice Gooseberry and Rhubarb Tarts - for her dinner next year - the chickens' were never Poked off again

And what was the end of the naughty Girl - Oh she - had to sit still - and do lessons - and the Cat laughed when she heard it - because - she didn't like a long stick to come after her - and the chickens said - Cock a doodle doo - we dont want any more of you - they meant the bad little Girl -

So she went on doing mischief - and tore her Frocks - and never said if you Please and never said thankyou - and walked in the mud - and bit off the ends of her Glove fingers - always - for she was dreadfully naughty - — the End — KG the same subjects, so, after that summer of 1890, we did not go out painting any more together. Whether days or months passed between our meetings, I was always sure of the same hearty greeting from her.

The last time I saw her was February 28, 1901, at the Fine Art Society. I thought she looked fairly well, and seemed so, though she spoke of having felt tired sometimes. But she said nothing of the serious illness of the year before . . . When later on in the year I called at her house, I was told she was not well enough to see friends.

Her work remains for all to see and enjoy. Of herself, I can truly say that she was one of the most honest, straightforward, and kindly of women: a sympathetic, true, and steadfast friend.

In 1889 Kate completed two books, besides the *Almanack* which by now was an institution: *Kate Greenaway's Book of Games*, with Edmund Evans as engraver and printer and Routledge & Sons publisher; and *The Royal Progress of King Pepito*, written by Beatrice F. Cresswell. In the *Book of Games* Kate could do what she wished, happy and un- restrained, but she found it hard, as usual, to assimilate another's ideas. The inelasticity of story-book illustrating seemed to paralyse her pencil and in *King Pepito* she became mannered and conventional.

This year Kate was elected a member of the Royal Institute of Painter in Water-Colours, and was represented by thirteen frames of drawings in the British Section of the International Exhibition at Paris (from the 1884 *Almanack, Marigold Garden*, the *Language of Flowers*, and *Little Ann*).

The last letter from Ruskin to Kate Greenaway was sent from Brant- wood on May 14, 1889, thus ending, as far as he was concerned, a correspondence which had not only been one of the greatest pleasures of Kate's life, but had been above all a healthy stimulus and a liberal education.

For the last year or two Kate Greenaway had been showing unmis- takable signs of failing energy, and in 1891 she published nothing other than the *Almanack*. However, for the first time she determined to hold a one-man exhibition of her water-colour drawings at the Gallery of the Fine Art Society at 148, New Bond Street. For the first time the general public and the critics had the opportunity of assigning to her her right- ful place among comtemporary artists. She had appeared in most of the important exhibitions in London and the provinces and her pictures had almost invariably found purchasers. Her works were known on two continents, and generally enthusiastic reviews and critiques of them appeared in such periodicals as *Le Figaro, Journal des Débats, Gazette des Beaux-Arts, National Zeitung,* and *Saturday Review.*

Now, her work could be gauged in bulk and there was a chorus of approval. She netted £964 from the sale of her pictures, and the exhibition was considered highly successful.

With the exception of the Almanacks, there were no new publications with Kate Greenaway's name on the title-page during 1892 and 1900. She exhibited her water colours, and in 1893 permitted the Almanack drawings to be used as designs for wall-paper. She was also busy fulfilling the current demand for book-plates, and designed many for her friends and their children. She painted portraits, and by this time was struggling with the problems of painting in oil.

In 1893 began Kate Greenaway's connection with the *Ladies Home Journal,* for whom she executed seven or eight beautiful little pen-and-ink drawings for illustrated verses by Laura E. Richards. These did much to enlarge her circle of American admirers, besides being highly remunerative.

Kate had composed verses from her earliest days. But it must not be supposed that she had any illusions about her literary gifts, even though competent critics expressed the opinion that there was poetic fancy and feeling in even her early work. Throughout her life she kept up this pastime, and four thick volumes of neatly written manuscript running to hundreds of pages testify to the industry with which she followed what she herself says proved to be a vain hope. A hundred telling themes are gaily launched in a sea of words, and all goes well until we are disturbed by a mixed metaphor, or faulty rhyme. Only here and there do we find a poem which is sustained and carried on successfully to the end.

In 1894 began for Kate one of her rare and highly valued intimacies—her friendship with Violet Dickinson. From that time forward the two ladies, one tall and slim beyond the average, the other as noticeably short and stout, were much in each other's company. Their correspondence was incessant and Kate Greenaway's pencil was generally requisitioned to give an added note of piquancy and fancy to the humorous invention of her written communications. During the hot July of 1896 she dashed off a sketch of herself enjoying the 'bliss' of a shower from a watering-can. In December she accounts for her temporary seclusion by a sketch of herself as a hermit, and a month later, still in the comic mood, she pictures herself in the throes of composition and writes: 'Dear [her method of addressing well-loved intimates, omitting their

Kate Greenaway in her studio, 1895

names], Yes, it is a fine thing to have a friend who writes lovely poems . . .?'

In 1895, which marks Kate's last appearance in the Royal Academy exhibitions, she was represented at the Liverpool Exhibition, at the Royal Institute of Painters in Water-Colours.

During these years much of Kate's time was spent on letter-writing. She always had one on hand for Ruskin, to which she would sit down at any odd moment between meals, exercise, and work despatching it as soon as the end of the sheet was reached. In 1896 the year's *Almanack* was published, with Edmund Evans still the engraver and the responsible man in the enterprise. It is impossible to estimate, even approximately by how much her popularity had been enhanced by his excellent work. Some idea of their partnership may be gathered from the fact that in the twenty years since 1878 there had issued from the press in book form alone 932,100 copies of their joint productions. How far this enormous number might be increased by Christmas cards and independent designs for magazines would be impossible to hazard a guess.

Kate Greenaway's most important work of 1896 consisted of commissions from Stuart M. Samuel, M. P., for a portrait of his daughter

Vera, and to design processions for the decorations of his nurseries. On April 13 she writes:

I cannot tell how much a drawing of your little girl would be. It depends on the sort of drawing you want. A small water-colour would be £25—a little girl like a book drawing £10. I can only do certain kinds of book-plates, nothing heraldic. I do not think I could do a book-plate to be sure it was a portrait. An ordinary book-plate is £5 or £6. I could only undertake to do a portrait *here*—the little girl would have to be brought to me.

In 1898 she completed the book-plate in colours for Vera; the pains she took were extraordinary—the child, the design, the introduction

On a letter to Violet Dickinson, showing the artist's comic vein

above: Portrait of
Vera Evelyn Samuel, 1896
left: Bookplate for
Vera Evelyn Samuel, 1898

of the wreath of roses with the hovering bees (from Stuart Samuel's own book-emblem), and the lettering, all received the utmost consideration. The lettering proved too much for her, as on the occasion when Ruskin so roundly trounced her; so she agreed to have the words designed for her by a professional letter-draughtsman for her to copy in her drawing. When it was finished she took the keenest interest in the reproduction, and she was highly flattered that Stuart Samuel decided to discard the 'three-colour process' and adopt the more precious but vastly more expensive photogravure on copper. In this case each separate impression is printed from a plate inked à *la poupèe*—that is to say, the artist-printer inks the plate with the various coloured inks carefully matched to the tones of the drawing; so that, when the plate is passed through the press only one copy can be obtained from each printing, and the plate has to be inked again. A few impressions, therefore—say ten, or thereabouts—cost as much as the original drawing, but the result justifies the expenditure. The reproduction here given is not from the drawing itself, but is a three-colour reproduction from the printed impression which has often been mistaken for the original. The artist was delighted, and wrote— 'How much I should like to do a book like this, but I suppose it is fearfully expensive. . . . It is really beautifully done.'

The demand for the Kate Greenaway *Almanacks* had ceased and the series was abandoned after the 1897 publication.

1898 saw the third exhibition of Kate's pictures at the Fine Art Society's Gallery, and again her showing was successful. Out of one hundred and twenty-seven little pictures, sixty-six found purchasers, the total receipts reaching the sum of £1,024.16s. (net profit: £645.)

In 1899 Kate devoted herself seriously to the painting of portraits in oil colours, and her letters of this year are full of the difficulties which beset her. In March she said good-bye to her friends the Tennysons, on Lord Tennyson's departure to take up the Governorship of South Australia. They never met again.

On Saturday, the January 20, 1900, the following entry which says so little, but meant so much to Kate Greenaway, appears in her diary:— 'Mr. Ruskin died to-day at 2:30 in the afternoon from influenza.' It was Stuart Samuel who broke the news to her. 'On Sunday,' she wrote to Mrs. Evans (Edmund Evans' wife), 'some people came in and said they had seen from the papers he was dead. I didn't believe it.' On the following day she wrote to M. H. Spielmann (co-author of the 1905 biography, Ed.):

63

'I'm dreadfully sorry about Mr. Ruskin's death. It was a great shock. I only heard from Mrs. Severn on Saturday morning; she said then he had influenza, but they did not think of any danger. I've heard again to-day— they only knew there was any fear of it being fatal between 10 and 11 Saturday morning: He died at half-past two, entirely painlessly all through. I feel it very much, for he was a great friend—and there is no one else like him.'

Spielmann writes that she opened her heart to him, who had also known Ruskin and loved him well. He points out that up until Ruskin's death, never in her letters did she write a word about her own ill-health, lest she should distress one for whom she had so affectionate and un-selfish a friendship.

Not wishing to leave her work with oils, Kate Greenaway turned down a request to contribute as a British Artist to the Paris Exhibition of 1900. Her health was failing, and causing her friends anxiety. She did under-take and was able to complete the illustration to *The April Baby's Book of Tunes* by the author of *Elizabeth and Her German Garden*, which was published towards the end of the year, but signs of failing power were only too evident. The *April Baby* illustrations were reproduced by chromo-lithography and therefore were inferior to Edmund Evans' inter-pretations. But the author was delighted, and wrote:

In answer to your letter I can only tell you that I did not, unfortunately, know Miss Kate Greenaway personally, and that while she was illustrating the *April Baby's Book of Tunes* we only occasionally wrote to each other about it. I felt quite sure that her pictures would be charming and did not like to bother her with letters of my own crude ideas. It was odd that, though she had never seen the babies or their photographs, her pictures were so much like what the babies were at that time that I have often been asked whether she had sketched them from life.

Her letters were exceedingly kind, and one of the April Baby's most precious possessions is a copy she sent her of *Marigold Garden* with a little pen-and-ink figure on the fly-leaf drawn specially for her. She wrote me that she had been ill for a long time and had not been able to work at my illus-trations, and that they had all been crowded into a few weeks at the end of the time given her by the publishers. She apparently thought they had suffered from this, but I think most people will agree that they are as charming as anything she ever did. Naturally I was extremely pleased to have the weaknesses of my story hidden behind such a pretty string of daintiness. So peculiarly simple and kind were her letters that even a stranger like myself who only knew her through them felt, when she died, that there was one sweet nature the less in the world.—Believe me, yours very truly,

The Author of 'Elizabeth and her German Garden.'

That she now rather shrank from undertaking work of this kind we have already seen from the letter written to M. H. Spielmann, who, as a friend of some years' standing, asked her if she would be disposed to illustrate one of his wife's stories which were appearing in *Little Folks*, and were afterwards published in book form. In the event, the book, which contains brilliant drawings by several leading black-and-white artists of the day, was not lacking in two from the pencil of Kate Green- away.

At the same time her letters are sadly eloquent of her failing health:

KATE GREENAWAY TO MRS. M. H. SPIELMANN

11 *Jan.* 1901.

It is so long since I have seen you—so long since I have been. It has not been my fault. I have not been well enough. I seem to have been ill all the year. I had a long illness all the autumn which I am not yet recovered from —and then colds so bad they have been illnesses. . . . I have seen no one hardly and done so little work. I'm so sorry when I don't work. For the time so soon goes and I always have so much I want to do.

Ruskin's birthday was on the 8th of February. On the first anniversary of it a year after his death, Kate wrote to Mrs. Severn:

On a letter to Ruskin

My dearest Joanie—Tomorrow is a sad day again. How I always wish I had done so much, much more. And I should have if life had not been so difficult to me of late years. . . .

If it would get warmer I could get out; then I should get stronger. As it is I take everything I can. This is the little programme: medicine, 9 times a day; beef tea, 8 times; port wine, champagne, brandy and soda, eggs and milk. I'm all day at it. Can I do more? Am I not a victim?

My dearest love to you. Your loving   Katie.

Yet in spite of her illness it must not be supposed that Kate's desire for industry ever flagged for a moment. She was full of schemes for books —not merely projected schemes, but plans fully matured, first sketches made, and pages fully 'set-out.' There was a new *Blake's Songs of Innocence*, to be published at a shilling net, each song with at least one drawing; this was so fully worked out that for certain of the designs several sketches were made. No fewer than twenty-two sketches were designed for a volume of *Nursery Rhymes*; there are fourteen to *Baby's Début*; and twelve and four respectively to Hans Christian Andersen's *Snow Queen* and *What the Moon Saw*. And, finally, A *Book of Girls* was to be illustrated with six of her daintiest pictures. A brave programme, ready to be carried into execution; but publishers were doubtful, and the schemes were not pursued.

Several friends sought to remove the discouragement under which Kate Greenaway was now labouring, in order to open up new vistas of activity. For some time she had herself schemed a great dressmaking business in her own name, with herself as designer; but it never got beyond the talking stage. Then she had the idea of modelling bas-reliefs in *gesso* for decorative purposes; but that also came to nothing. For her heart was in her drawing and painting, and she welcomed cordially a suggestion that the Editor of the *Magazine of Art* should write an article on 'The Later Work of Kate Greenaway,' partly in order to draw public attention to her oil-painting, but mainly to bring forward once more her name as an active art-worker, for she was firmly persuaded that she was well-nigh forgotten—'forgotten,' the bitterest word in all the vocabulary to one who has been a public favourite and whose name has rung throughout the world.

Then, in August of 1901, Miss Greenaway was offered the post of editor of a new Magazine for children at a handsome salary, but she refused it. Only three short months were to pass before 'finis' was to be written both to work and life.

66

A fortnight before she had written to Mrs. Stuart Samuel from Cromer:

I've been very ill—acute muscular rheumatism—horribly painful. I am now, I hope, getting better. It has been so in my mind the wish to write to you. You were so kind, it felt ungrateful to disappear in silence. . . . —Your affectionate   KATE GREENAWAY.

And again, ten days before she passed away:

'I should love a drive when I'm well enough. I will write and tell you how I get on; then, if you will, take me one day. With my love.'

But the end came, at 39, Frognal, on November 6th.

The privacy she wished for in life was observed at her death; only a few friends attended in the Chapel of the Cremation Society's Cemetery at Woking, on November 12th; fewer still on the day following, when the casket was quietly interred at Hampstead.

(Editor's Note: KATE GREENAWAY by M. H. Spielmann and G. S. Layard [Adam and Charles Black, London, 1905] has provided nearly all the material for this section, and for the later section containing some of the correspondence between Kate Greenaway and John Ruskin. Whenever possible, the actual words of the Spielmann-Layard biography have been used; sometimes its authors quote from Kate Greenaway's own notes for an autobiography, sometimes they use her own words transposed into the third person. With the exception of one or two comments or facts of my own, and some change of order, this is entirely faithful to the 1905 work.)

ARTIST AND CRITIC

A Selection of Letters to and from John Ruskin

R USKIN'S letters to K. G. numbered about 500, and covered the period from 1880 until the final one dated May 14, 1889. K. G. continued writing to him (her letters totalled perhaps 1,000) almost daily until his death in 1900.

Ruskin seems to have destroyed all K. G.'s letters save perhaps one before 1886. She, on the other hand, appears to have kept every scrap of Ruskin's writing, and even treasured the numerous telegrams which he sent her on special occasions, for Ruskin loved the telegraph.

BRANTWOOD, CONISTON,
Jan. 6th. 1879 [a mistake for 1880].

My dear Miss Greenaway—I lay awake half (no a quarter) of last night thinking of the hundred things I want to say to you–and never shall get said!–and I'm giddy and weary–and now can't say even half or a quarter of one out of the hundred. They're about you–and your gifts–and your fancies –and your–yes–perhaps one or two little tiny faults:– and about other people children, and grey-haired, and what you could do for them—if you once made up your mind for whom you would do it. For children *only* for instance?–or for old people, *me* for instance–and *of* children and old people– whether for those of 1880–only–or of 18–8–9–10–11–12–20–0–0—0–0, etc. etc. etc. Or more simply annual or perennial.

Well, of the thousand things–it was nearer a thousand than a hundred– this is anyhow the first. Will you please tell me whether you can only draw these things out of your head–or could, if you chose, draw them with the necessary modifications from nature? For instance–Down in Kent the other day I saw many more lovely farm-houses–many more pretty landscapes–

68

than any in your book. But the farms had, perhaps, a steam-engine in the yard—the landscapes a railroad in the valley. Now, do you never want to draw such houses and places, as they used to be, and might be?

That's No. 1.

No. 2 of the thousand.

Do you only draw pretty children out of your head? In my parish school there are at least twenty prettier than any in your book–but they are in costumes neither graceful nor comic–they are not like blue china–they are not like mushrooms—they are like–very ill-dressed Angels. Could you draw groups of these as they *are*?

No. 3 of the thousand.

Did you ever see a book called Flitters, Tatters, and the Councillor?

No. 4 of the thousand.

Do you ever see the blue sky? and when you do, do you like it?

No. 5.

Is a witch's ride on a broomstick the only chivalry you think it desirable to remind the glorious Nineteenth Century of?

No. 6.—Do you believe in Fairies?

No. 7.—In ghosts?

No. 8.—In Principalities or Powers?

No. 9.—In Heaven?

No. 10.—In Any where else?

No. 11.—Did you ever see Chartres Cathedral?

No. 12.—Did you ever study, there or elsewhere, thirteenth century glass?

No. 13.—Do you ever go to the MS. room of the British Museum?

No. 14.—Heavy outline will not go with strong colour–but if so, do you never intend to draw with delicate outline?

No. 15.—Will you please forgive me–and tell me–some of those things I've asked?—Ever gratefully yours,   J. RUSKIN.

To this letter Miss Greenaway responded at once, and he writes again:—

BRANTWOOD, CONISTON,
Jan. 15th. 1880.

Dear Miss Greenaway—How delightful of you to answer all my questions!–and to read *Fors!* I never dreamed you were one of my readers—and I had rather you read that than anything else of mine, and rather *you* read it than anybody else.

I am so delighted also with your really liking blue sky–and those actual cottages, and that you've never been abroad. And that's all I can say to-day, but only this, that I think from what you tell me, you will feel with me, in my wanting you to try the experiment of representing any actual piece of nature (however little) as it really is, yet in the modified harmony of colour necessary for printing–making a simple study first as an ordinary water-colour sketch, and then translating it into outline and the few advisable tints, so as to be able to say–The sun was in or out,–it was here, or there, and the gown, or the paling, was of this colour on one side, and of that on the other.

I believe your lovely design and groupings will come out all the brighter and richer for such exercise. And then–when the question of absolute translation is once answered, that of conventional change may be met on its separate terms, securely.—Ever gratefully yours, J. RUSKIN.

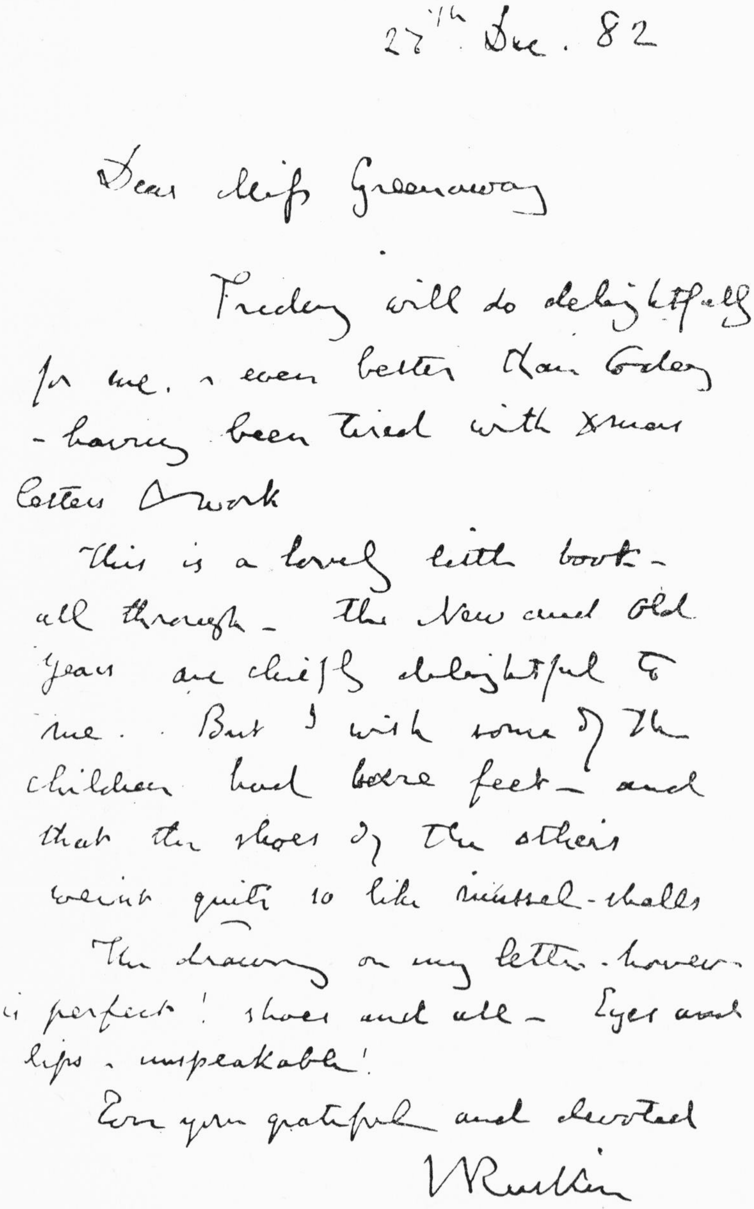

27ᵗʰ Dec. 82

Dear Miss Greenaway

Friday will do delightfully for me, – even better than today – having been tired with xmas letters & work

This is a lovely little book – all through – The New and Old Years are chiefly delightful to me. But I wish some of the children had bare feet – and that the shoes of the others weren't quite so like mussel-shells

The drawing on my letter, however, is perfect! shoes and all – Eyes and lips – unspeakable!

Ever your grateful and devoted
J Ruskin

Facsimile of Ruskin's letter
of December 27, 1882

After receiving, in a spirit less critical than some, his copy of *A Day in a Child's Life*, Ruskin wrote:

BRANTWOOD, CONISTON,
Christmas Day, 1881.

My dear Miss Greenaway—You are the first friend to whom I write this morning; and among the few to whom I look for real sympathy and help. You are fast becoming–I believe you are already, except only Edward B. Jones–the helpfullest in showing me that there are yet living souls on earth who can see beauty and peace and Good-will among men–and rejoice in them.

You have sent me a little choir of such angels as are ready to sing, if we listen, for Christ's being born–every day.

I trust you may long be spared to do such lovely things, and be an element of the best happiness in every English household that still has an English heart, as you are already in the simpler homes of Germany.

To my mind Ludwig Richter and you are the only real philosophers and —— of the Nineteenth Century.

I'll write more in a day or two about many things that I want to say respecting the possible range of your subjects. I was made so specially happy yesterday by finding Herrick's Grace among the little poems—but they are all delightful.—Ever gratefully and affectionately yours,   J. RUSKIN.

After K. G. suggested a date for their first meeting, Ruskin wrote:

27th, Dec. 82.

Dear Miss Greenaway—Friday will do delightfully for me,–even better than to-day–having been tired with Xmas letters and work.

This is a lovely little book–all through–the New and Old Years are chiefly delightful to me. But I wish some of the children had bare feet–and that the shoes of the others weren't *quite* so like mussel-shells.

The drawing on my letter however is perfect! shoes and all–eyes and lips –unspeakable.—Ever your grateful and devoted.   J. RUSKIN.

In 1883 Ruskin accepted his second call to the Oxford Professorship, interrupted in 1879 by ill-health, and gave his first series of lectures on the Art of England. He wrote to Kate at this time.

On May 11 he writes:

I can't write a word but this to-night.—I'll think over the drawing-cleaning; perhaps it will be safest to trust it only to you–there's plenty of time, for *your* lecture isn't till the 23rd,—we shall have had our tea long before that.

I can't part with the drawings to be india Rd [india-rubbered]—having them by me helps me so, and I'm going to put those which I show—(I'm only going to show what I *speak* of, to prevent carelessness in looking) under raised mounts which will quite hide soiled edges.

On June 7th:

You are *not* to put any more sugar-plums of sketches in your letters–as if they weren't sweet enough without. Besides, I can't have you wasting your time and wits in that scattered dew of fancy.—You must really gather yourself into a real rivulet between banks in perspective–and reflect everything truly that you see.

You absurd Kate to think I was tired of the drawings. I was only tired of seeing the corners unfinished–you're nearly as bad as me, that way. Now be a good girl and draw some flowers that won't look as if their leaves had been in curlpapers all night–and some more chairs than that one chair–with the shade all right and the legs all square–and then I'll tell you what you must do next.

Again on the 15th:

I'm thinking of you every day and a great part of the day long, whenever I get out into the fields, more and more anxious every day that you should resolve on a summer's work of utter veracity–drawing–no matter what,–*but* as it *is*.

I am certain all your imagination would expand afterwards, like—a rosebud. But especially I do want some children as they are,—and that you should be able to draw a pretty one without mittens, and that you should be more interested in phases of character. I want your exquisite feeling given to teach—not merely to amuse . . . You'll soon have proof of the lecture on you!

On June 17th, he writes from Oxford:

What a lovely little bit of dark grounded grace! and the two pencils are delicious–but the feet *are* getting *too* small.

It's delighted to me beyond telling that you do yourself feel the need of a time of obedience to the 'everlasting Yea' of Things.—What I meant by phases of character was—in painting, what Scott or Shakespeare give in words,—the differences in loveliness which are endless in humanity. Those little girls who were playing at being in church must have been so different from little girls who were tormented by being at church.

Yes, it is very sad that I can't get done here,—but there are three years of absence to redeem, and being allowed in my own department to have my

Pencil Sketch

own way entirely, it is a very stringent duty to do the best I can. And just think what the arrangements of a system of teaching in connection with a great University means, or *should* mean.

I have mounted, for the present, 25 of the Mother Goose drawings beside the plates, and put them in a cabinet by themselves, among our loan series. People are immensely interested in them, and feel the difference between drawing and plate quite as you would like them to. Every drawing has its own sliding frame and glass so that they are *absolutely* safe, as far as handling is concerned . . .

I shall very soon have a proof of lecture for you.

And from Brantwood on the 22nd:

What lovely, lovely things these are, that have come to-day–the tambourine and the looking out to sea.—But your own eyes ought to have been three times as big–on your eyes be it–and I don't understand the doggie carrying the maulstick–because I've never seen you with a pet in a blue riband–and the first thing I should have done would have been to order the feathers out of your hat! . . .

I got tired at Oxford and had to run down here for some rest–but shall be up again in a week or two and I hope in the mean time to get some things organised for engraving some of the line sketches in line.

From Brantwood:

My dear Kate,—(see my third lecture sent you to-day)—it *is* absolutely necessary for you to be–now–sometimes, Classical.—I return you–though heartbrokenly (for the day)–one of those three sylphs, come this morning.

Will you—(it's all for your own good!) make her stand up, and then draw her for me without her hat–and, without her shoes,–because of the heels) and without her mittens, and without her–frock and its frill? And let me see exactly how tall she is–and how–round. [Note written in pencil: 'Do nothing of the kind. J.R.S.'] (his niece, Joan Severn).

It will be *so* good of–and for–you—And to, and for–me.

After finishing this letter, he has turned it over and written:

5th July.

Finished right side yesterday. Posted 6th. That naughty Joan got hold of it–never mind her–you see, she doesn't like the word 'round'–that's all.

In John Ruskin's 'Lecture on Mrs. Allingham and Kate Greenaway,' delivered at Oxford and printed in *The Art of England* (published by George Allen), he said:

73

New Year's greeting for John Ruskin, 1886

I may best indicate to you the grasp which the genius of Miss Kate Greenaway has taken upon the spirits of foreign lands, no less than her own, by
translating the last paragraph of the entirely candid, and intimately observant, review of modern English art given by Monsieur Ernest Chesneau,
in his small volume, *La Peinture Anglaise*. . . .

He gives first a lovely passage (too long to introduce now) upon the
gentleness of the satire of John Leech, as opposed to the bitter malignity
of former caricature. Then he goes on: 'The great softening of the English
mind, so manifest already in John Leech, shows itself in a decisive manner
by the enthusiasm with which the public have lately received the designs
of Mr. Walter Crane, Mr. Caldecott, and Miss Kate Greenaway. The two
first-named artists began by addressing to children the stories of Perrault
and of the *Arabian Nights*, translated and adorned for them in a dazzling
manner; and, in the works of all these three artists, landscape plays an important part;—familiar landscape, very English, interpreted with a "bon-
homie savante"' (no translating that), 'spiritual, decorative in the rarest
sense—strange and precious adaptation of Etruscan art, Flemish and Japanese, reaching, together with the perfect interpretation of nature, to in-
comparable chords of colour harmony. These powers are found in the work
of the three, but Miss Greenaway, with a profound sentiment of love for
children, puts the child alone on the scene, companions him in all his

74

solitudes, and shows the infantine nature in all its naïveté, its gaucherie, its touching grace, its shy alarm, its discoveries, ravishments, embarrassments, and victories; the stumblings of it in wintry ways, the enchanted smiles of its spring-time, and all the history of its fond heart and guileless egoism.

'From the honest but fierce laugh of the coarse Saxon, William Hogarth, to the delicious smile of Kate Greenaway, there has past a century and a half. Is it the same people which applauds to-day the sweet genius and tender malices of the one, and which applauded the bitter genius and slaughterous satire of the other? After all, that is possible—the hatred of vice is only another manifestation of the love of innocence.' . . .

I have brought with me to-day in the first place some examples of her pencil sketches in primary design. . . . You have here for consummate example, a dance of fairies under a mushroom, which she did under challenge to show me what fairies were like. 'They'll be very like children,' she said. I answered that I didn't mind, and should like to see them all the same;—so here they are, with a dance, also, of two girlies, outside of a mushroom; and I don't know whether the elfins or girls are the fairyfootedest: and one or two more subjects, which you may find out;—but in all you will see that the line is ineffably tender and delicate, and can't in the least be represented by the lines of a woodcut. . . . (From a letter written in 1879 it will be seen that the heaviness of her line had before been a matter of complaint with him.)

So far of pure outline. Next, for the enrichment of it by colour. Monsieur Chesneau doubts if the charm of Miss Greenaway's work can be carried farther. I answer, with security,—yes, very much farther, and that in two directions: first, in her own method of design; and secondly, the manner of its representation in printing.

First, her own design has been greatly restricted by being too ornamental, or, in our modern phrase, decorative;—contracted into any corner of a Christmas card, or stretched like an elastic band round the edges of an almanac. Now her art is much too good to be used merely for illumination; it is essentially and perfectly that of true colour-picture, and that the most naïve and delightful manner of picture, because, on the simplest terms, it comes nearest reality. No end of mischief has been done to modern art by the habit of running semi-pictorial illustration round the margins of ornamental volumes, and Miss Greenaway has been wasting her strength too sorrowfully in making the edges of her little birthday-books, and the like, glitter with unregarded gold, whereas her power should be concentrated in the direct illustration of connected story, and her pictures should be made complete on the page, and far more realistic than decorative. There is no charm so enduring as that of the real representation of any given scene; her present designs are like living flowers flattened to go into an herbarium,

On a letter to Ruskin

and sometimes too pretty to be believed. We must ask her for more descriptive reality, for more convincing simplicity, and we must get her to organise a school of colourists by hand, who can absolutely facsimile her own first drawing.

This is the second matter on which I have to insist. I bring with me to-day twelve of her original drawings, and have mounted beside them, good impressions of the published prints.

I may heartily congratulate both the publishers and possessors of the book on the excellence of these; yet if you examine them closely, you will find that the colour blocks of the print sometimes slip a little aside, so as to lose the precision of the drawing in important places; and in many other respects better can be done, in at least a certain number of chosen copies. I must not, however, detain you to-day by entering into particulars in this matter. I am content to ask your sympathy in the endeavour, if I can prevail on the artist to undertake it.

Only if respect to this and every other question of method in engraving, observe further that *all* the drawings I bring you to-day agree in one thing, —minuteness and delicacy of touch carried to its utmost limit, visible in its perfectness to the eyes of youth, but neither executed with a magnifying glass nor, except to aged eyes, needing one. Even I, at sixty-four, can see the essential qualities of the work without spectacles; though only the youngest of my friends here can see, for example, Kate's fairy dance, perfectly, but *they* can with their own bright eyes.

The following extract from a letter of Ruskin's dated 'Brantwood, 26th December '83' refers to the headpiece of Letter 93 of *Fors:—*

I shan't go to sleep over your note to-day.

But I have no words any more than if I *was* asleep, to tell you how marvellous I think these drawings. No one has ever done anything equal

On a letter to Ruskin

to them in pure grace of movement–no one in exquisiteness of dainty design–I tremble now to ask you to draw in any other way.

As for the gift of them, I had never such a treasure given me, in my life–but it is not for me only. I am sure that these drawings will be [valued] endlessly and everywhere if I can get them engraved the least rightly,—the sight of them alters one's thoughts of all the world.

The little beauty with the note, alone, would have made a Christmas for me.

I hope you will like the use I've made of one of your little dance-maidens –I think her glory of simplicity comes well alone.

The Ruskin letters of 1884 are full of interest. Criticism, appreciation, good-humoured chaff, and sadness, jostle one another at every turn. On July 6th, referring to an illustration she is engaged on for *Marigold Garden*, he adds instruction to praise:

You're a good girl to draw that leaf. The four princesses in green tower will be delightful but the *first thing* you have to do in this leafy world is to learn to paint a leaf green, of its full size, at one blow, as a fresco painter does it on a background, with the loaded brush opening by pressure to the leaf's full breadth and closing to its point.

Again on the 9th:

I knew you could do it, if you only would. That's been what's making me so what you call angry lately. This is as good as well can be. Only, remember brown is only to be used for actual earth, and where plants grow close to it or for brown dark leaves etc., not as shadow. And there's already more delineation than I at present want you to spend time in.

And on the 25th he continues his instruction:

The ivy is very beautiful and you have taken no end of useful trouble with it, but the colour is vapid and the leaves too shiny. Shine is always vulgar except on hair and water–it spoils leaves as much as it does flesh–and even jewels are better without it. I shall return you this study which you will find very useful and I've sent you two more sods to-day, more to be enjoyed than painted–if you like to do a bit of one, well and good.

I am glad to hear of the oil work–but it is winter work not summer. I can't think how you can bear to spoil summer air with it.

On October 18, he says:

K. G. worried by a stray puppy.
On a letter to Ruskin

You must like Turner as soon as you see landscape completely. His affections—or prejudices, I do not wish or expect you to like—any more than I should have expected him to like roses drawn like truffles.

Then he finds that he has been expecting too much, counting on physical powers with which Kate has not been endowed.

I have not enough allowed for your being nearsighted but shall like to see what you do see. At any rate near or far off, study of the relation of moss is indispensable.

Those hot colours of flowers are very lovely–you can do as many as you like–only not dull things mixed with Naples yellow.

Look well at the foot of Corregio's Venus, and at the weeds in Mantegna's foreground.

Ruskin's unqualified praise was rare, usually coinciding with an improvement in his health.

11th. Feb., 84.

I did not answer your question which of the girlies I liked best because it was unanswerable, yet something is to be said anent it.

Of course the Queen of them all is the little one in front–but she's just a month or six weeks too young for *me*. Then there's the staff bearer on the right (—the left, as they come) turning round ! ! !–but she's just three days and a minute or two too *old* for me. Then there's the divine one with the dark hair, and the beatific one with the brown,–but I think *they've* both got lovers already and have only come to please the rest, and wouldn't be mine if I prayed them ever so. Then there is the little led beauty who is ruby and diamond in one,–but–but,–not quite tall enough, again–I think the wisest choice will be the pale one between the beatific and the divine!

But they're all ineffable!–I think you never did a more marvellous piece of beauty and it's a treasure to me like a caught dream.

I wonder how you can bear to think of drawing *me*—and how you mean to do it!

Sitting always tires me a good deal, but perhaps John will let me lie down in his room for a quarter of an hour before tea.

Of this portrait he writes later in an undated letter of the same year:

I was with some saucy girls yesterday and I was saying how proud I was to have my portrait drawn by you–but only I had been so sleepy!

If the portrait was ever done, there is now no trace of it.

He writes of an exhibition and further projects:

I was so curious to see those Grosvenor pictures that I went in with Joan yesterday and got a glimpse.—The only picture there worth looking at is Millais' Lorne, and his straddling girl is a fright, and his Lady Campbell a horror.—As for that somebody in the sea, what did I tell you about model drawing?—People are getting absolutely brutified by it. There's another nearly as bad in the Suffolk St. In the great mediæval times, painters could draw people dressed or undressed just as they chose–without the smallest weakness, shame, or conceit. Now, there is scarcely a foolish or bad feeling in one's head or body, that isn't made worse in the model-room. I scratched nearly every picture through in my catalogue yesterday.

On a letter to Ruskin

Ruskin's comment here is of special interest because his wife had left him for John Millais.

Sometimes Ruskin is betrayed into writing about himself. For example on March 20th, from Brantwood, when for the time being not only all the world seems wrong but in Professor Clifford's poignant words even 'The Great Companion' seems dead:

I didn't tell you if I was well—I'm not: nor have I been for some time,– a very steady gloom on me; not stomach depression but the sadness of deliberately preparing for the close of life—drawing in, or giving up, all one's plans—thinking of one's beloved places, I shall never be there again–and so on. A great deal of the time I *have* lost in the mere friction of life– scarcely any sense of Peace,—And no hope of any life to come. I forget it all more in the theatre than anywhere—cathedrals are no good any more!

BRANTWOOD [*March* 22, 1884].

What a nice letter—and I'm so pleased that your Father was surprised, and that Johnnie liked 'Unto This Last'– and that you think you'll like some more. I think I tired myself with trying to draw your little girlie yes- terday–she's *so* hard, and I'm as lazy to-day as ever I can be, and don't care for anything but a French Novel, about police! And I'm ashamed to read it at 3 in the afternoon–and it's wet–and I can't do St. George's accounts– and I should like some tea and muffins–and–there are no muffins in Conis- ton. . . . I feel so listless because there's no time left now to do anything.

Oh dear, think how happy you are with all that power of drawing–and ages to come to work in and paint Floras and Norahs and Fairies and Mary's and Goddesses and–bodices–oh me, when will you do me one with- out any?

I must take to my French novel, there's no help for it—Mercy on us, and it's two hours to teatime! and the room so quiet, and all my books and things about me—and I can't do a thing—

Wouldn't you like a photograph of me like that?

Rover is indisposed
and has to be bandaged.
On a letter to Ruskin

No doubt, it is difficult to help feeling at times that Ruskin's admiration for K. G. partakes too much of hyperbole. And yet we cannot but confess that as he was honest in welcoming the Pre-Raphaelites so was he honest in his greeting of her. He was weary of the artificial pedantry of those who had elaborated an artistic code 'with titles and sub-titles applicable to every form of [art] and tyrannous over every mode of sentiment,' and he acclaimed an exquisite small voice, which sang its little song in its own sweet tone of purity and in its own tender unconventional way. What he meant was in no wise that she was cleverer than other people. He over and over again tells her one way or another that she was no great executant. But she had that rarer gift of seeing old things through new eyes and giving artistic expression with curious and delightful success to these newer and fresher views. And as Ruskin was by nature vehement and by practice a controversialist, he could scarcely resist being led from time to time into italicizing his words and emphasizing his verdicts.

Ruskin is full of schemes for projects with Kate Greenaway. One of the 'lovely plans' he has in his head is 'a book on botany for you and me to do together—you do the plates and I the text—a hand-book of field botany. It will be such a rest for you and such a help for—everybody!—chiefly me.'

But it comes to nothing.

On Dec. 1st Ruskin writes from Oxford:

I've been in a hard battle here these eight weeks,–the atheistic scientists all against me, and the young men careless and everything going wrong–so that I have had to fight with sadness and anger in all my work. My last lecture is to be given to-morrow but I have been feeling more tired in this cold weather, and the correspondence is terrible. I have never a moment to draw or do anything I like–except throw myself on my bed and rest, or listen to any good music if I can get it quietly.

Ruskin now retired into seclusion at Brantwood, where he was as happy as failing health would permit in the company of Mrs. Arthur Severn, the 'Joan' of the letters, and her husband and family who lived with him.

Now it was that he set to work on that remarkable fragment of autobiography published at intervals under the title of *Praeterita*.

BRANTWOOD, 19 *Jan.* 85.

The book I send to-day is of course much more completed in shade than your outlines ever need, or ought to be, but I believe you would find ex-

80

treme benefit in getting into the habit of studying from nature with the pen point in this manner and forcing yourself to complete the study of a head, cap, hair and all–whether it succeeded or not to your mind, in the time you now give to draw the profile of lips and chin.

You never need fear losing refinement,–you would gain steadily in fancy, knowledge and power of expression of solid form, and complex character. Note especially in these drawings that their expressional power depends on the rightness, not the delicacy of their lines, and is itself most subtle where *they* are most forcible. In the recording angels, pages 22, 23, the face of 23 is beautiful because its lines are distinct–22 fails wholly because the faint proof of the plate has dimmed them.

Tell me what the publishers 'propose' now, that I may sympathise in your indignation–and 'propose' something very different.

I can scarcely conceive any sale paying the expenses of such a book as the Language of Flowers–but think you could produce one easily with the original outlay of–say at the outsidest, £500, which you would sell 50,000 of at a shilling each in a month.

Tell me how you like this little head and tail piece herewith. I'm going to use them for a little separate pamphlets on schools.

The following month he writes:

¼ past two P.M. 13 *Feb.* 85. BRANTWOOD.

Am I busy? Well–you shall just hear what I've done to-day.

7–½ past, Coffee. Read Northcote's conversations marking extracts for lecture.

½ 7–8. Dress.

8–½ past, Write two pages of autobiography.

½ past 8–¼ 9. Lesson to Jane Anne on spelling and aspiration. Advise her to get out of the habit of spelling at, hat.

¼ 9–half past. Correct press of chapter of Modern Painters.

½ 9–½ 10. Breakfast–read letters–devise answers to smash a book-seller, and please an evangelical clergyman–also to make Kate understand what I'm about and put Joan's mind at ease. . . .

Wished I had been at the Circus. Tried to fancy Clemmie 'all eyes.' Thought a little mouth and neck might be as well besides. Pulled grape hyacinth out of box, and put it in water. Why isn't it blue?

½ 10. Set to work again. Finished revise of M. P. chapter. Then took up

Pencil sketch

Miss Alex. next number. Fitted pages etc. Wrote to Miss A. to advise her of proof coming.

Wrote to Clergyman and Joan and smashed bookseller.

½ 12. Examined chess game by correspondence. Sent enemy a move. Don't think she's much chance left.

1. Looked out some crystals, 'Irish Diamonds' for school at Cork. Meditated on enclosed mistress' and pupils' letters–still to be answered before resting—Query, how?

¼ past one. Lunch. Peasoup.

¼ to two. Meditate letter to Colonel Brackenbury on the Bride of Abydos. Meditate what's to be said to K.

2. Baxter comes in–receives directions for manifold parcels and Irish diamonds–think I may as well write this, thus. Wild rainy day. Wrote Col. Brackenbury while your ink was drying to turn leaves–now for Irish Governess,–and my mineralogist–and that's all!

After Kate Greenaway has moved to Hampstead (February, 1885), Ruskin writes:

I hope you are beginning by this time in the afternoon to be very happy in thinking you're really at home on the Hill, now,–and that you will find all the drawers slide nicely, corners fit and firesides cosy, and that the flowers are behaving prettily, and the chimnies–draw–as well as you.— That's a new pun, all my own–only think! It isn't a very complimentary one–but indeed–the first thing to be seriously thought of in a new house is chimnies,–one can knock windows out–or partitions down–build out oriels–and throw up turrets–but never make a chimney go that don't choose.

Anyhow—I am glad you are settled somewhere–and that I shan't have my letters to direct nobody knows where.—And let us bid, both, farewell to hollow ways, that lead only to disappointment–and know what we're about,–and not think truths teazing, but enjoy each other's sympathy and admiration–and think always–how nice we are!

On a letter to Ruskin

The year 1885 also saw the publication of *Dame Wiggins of Lea and her Seven Wonderful Cats. A humorous tale, written principally by a lady of ninety*, edited with additional verses by Ruskin, and with some new illustrations by Kate Greenaway.

In the letters preceding the publication of *Dame Wiggins*, which by the way in *Praeterita* Ruskin designates his 'calf-milk of books on the lighter side,' we find several references to K. G.'s illustrations.

In May he writes: 'Don't bother yourself with Dame Wiggins—it's the cats you'll break down in.' But his prophecy proved wrong, for on July 5 he confesses 'you never shewed such sense in anything as in doing those cats'; and again on the 11th, 'The cats are gone to be wood-cutted just as they are—they can't be better'; and again on the 29th, alluding to a further proposed collaboration: 'We'll do that book together of course—I'll write a story about perpetual spring—but—however are you to learn what a lamb's like? However after those D. W. cats I feel that nothing's impossible.'

In mid-summer of 1885 Ruskin was gravely ill (see text.), but by January of the next year had sufficiently recovered to resume work on his autobiography. He wrote on the 22nd:

> I am so very thankful you like this eighth number so much, for I was afraid it would begin to shock people. I have great pleasure in the thing myself—it is so much easier and simpler to say things face to face like that, than as an author. The ninth has come out very prettily, I think—

Again on the 27th:

> I am so very very glad you like Præterita—for it is—as you say—the 'natural' me—only of course peeled carefully—It is different from what else I write because—you know—I seldom have had to describe any but heroic—or evil—characters—and this watercress characters is so much easier to do—and credible and tasteable by everybody's own lips.

On November 30 Kate wrote (one of the very few letters before 1887 preserved by Ruskin):

> 'Well, I hope you're feeling better. I hope I will have a letter in the morning. I have enjoyed the *Praeterita* very much, it is so cheering to have it coming again . . .

And on Feb. 23rd:

83

On a letter to Ruskin

KG. 9 Feb. 1890
Many Happy returns of the day

"Many Happy Returns
of the Day."
A birthday greeting
for John Ruskin, 1890

It *is* lovely of you thinking of illustrating the life–I am greatly set up in
the thought of it. But wait a while. I hope it will be all more or less graceful. But I fear it will not be cheerful enough. I'll try and keep it as Katish
as–the *very* truth can be.

In 1886 Ruskin has a new scheme:

BRANTWOOD,
Saturday [Nov. 2, 1886].

It rejoices me so that you enjoy those old master drawings.

It comes, in the very moment when I wanted it–this British M. enthusiasm of yours.

I'm going to set up a girls' drawing school in London–a room where nice
young girls can go–and find no disagreeable people or ugly pictures. They
must all be introduced by some of my own sweetest friends–by K. G., by
Lilias T., by Margaret B. J. (Burne-Jones)–by my own sec. Lolly–or by
such as ever and anon may be enrolled as Honorary Students.

And I want you at once to choose, and buy for me beginning with
enclosed cheque, all the drawings by the old masters reproduced to your

84

good pleasure—Whatever you like, I shall–and the school will be far happier and more confident in your choice ratified by mine.

And I will talk over every bit of the plan with you–as you have time to think of it.

—I'm not quite sure I shall like *this* American book as well as Bret Harte –but am thankful for anything to make me laugh,–if it does.

Early in 1887 Ruskin set himself the task of teaching Kate Greenaway perspective in about a dozen consecutive letters, filling them with diagrams of cubes and gables and arches, and sparing no pains to make things plain to her. The calm violation of the laws of perspective in some of her earlier work was not due to quaintness. But in the spring of that year illness again laid him low. He went to Sandgate to recuperate, and writes Kate from there:

> You cannot conceive how in my present state, I envy–that is to say only in the strongest way, long for–the least vestige of imagination, such as yours. When nothing shows itself to me–all day long–but the dull room or the wild sea and I think what it must be to you to have far sight into dreamlands of truth–and to be able to see such scenes of the most exquisite grace and life and quaint vivacity–whether you draw them or not, what a blessing to have them there–at your call. And then I stopped and have been lying back in my chair the last quarter of an hour,–thinking–If I could only let you feel for only a quarter of an hour what it is to have no imagination–no power of calling up lovely things–no guidance of pencil point along the visionary line–Oh how thankful you would be to find your mind again.
>
> And what lovely work you have spent–where no one will ever see it but poor me—on the lightest of your messages. Do you remember the invitation sent by the girl holding the muffin high on her toasting fork? You never did a more careful or perfect profile. And the clusters of beauty in those festival or farewell ones?
>
> Well, I had joy out of them–such as you meant–and more than ever I could tell you, nor do I ever cease to rejoice at and wonder at them,–but with such sorrow that they are not all in a great lovely book, for all the world's New Years and Easter days.
>
> You might do a book of Festas, one of these days–with such processions!

By 'processions' are meant the long drawings with a bevy of following maids. They contain some of Miss Greenaway's most careful and dainty work in drawing, colour, and composition.

In 1888 Ruskin made his last foreign tour in hopes of renewing his health. He returned early in 1889 to Brantwood, with ten pathetic years

85

of growing infirmity before him. In May he was able to write Kate Greenaway a few letters, the last he was ever to send:

BRANTWOOD May-day 1889.

I've been a-maying with you all day,–coming upon one beautiful thing after another in my drawer, so long unopened–most thankfully to-day unlocked again–and sending balm and rose and lily sweetness all through the old study. What exquisite drawings those were you did just before I fell so ill,–the children passing under the flower arch–&c.! and Joan tells me you are doing *such* lovely things now with such background,–grander than ever, and of course the Piper is the best book you ever did–the Piper himself unsurpassable–and I feel as if he had piped me back out of the hill again, and would give some spring times yet to rejoice in your lovely work and its witness to them.

I do hope much, now–the change is greater and deeper for good than it has ever been before, but I have to watch almost every breath lest I should fall back again.

I wonder if you would care to come down in the wild rose time–and draw a branch or two, with the blue hills seen through them, and perhaps study a little falling water–or running–in the green shadows. I wouldn't set you to horrid work in the study, you should even draw any quantity of those things that you like–in the forenoon–and have tea in the study, and perhaps we could go on with the Swiss fish story!

BRANTWOOD, 3 May, 1889.

I am so very thankful that you can come–and still care to come–! I was so afraid you might have some work on hand that would hinder you–but now, I do trust that you will be quite happy, for indeed you will find here, when you are at liberty to do what you like best,–the exact things that become most tractable in their infinite beauty. You are doing great work already–some of the pages of the Piper are magnificent pictures, though with a white background–you will be led by the blue mountains and in the green glens to a deeper colourmelody–and–to how much else–there is no calculating. Please bring the primrose picture!–it will be the intensest delight to me and in looking over your drawings again, (how many do you think there are in my Kate drawer, now–besides those in the cabinets?) I feel more than ever—I might almost say twice as much as I used to, their altogether unrivalled loveliness.

And I think, as soon as you have seen all the exhibitions, and feel able to pack your country dresses and sacrifice London gaieties for monastic peace in art and nature, that you should really come; the roses will soon be here–and the gentians and hyacinths will certainly be here before you– and it is best, while all things bid fair for us, to take Fortune at her word.

86

I trust that my health will go on improving–but I might take cold, or Joanie might–or the children. At present we're all right and I want you to come as soon as may be.

His last letter:

BRANTWOOD, 14 *May*, 1889.

I am so very happy you are teaching yourself French. It is the greatest addition you can give to the happiness of your life,–some day I hope–old as I am–to see you drawing French children–and listening to them!

And you must learn a little Latin too! only to enjoy the nomenclature of Proserpina. Please take it down and read pages 227, 228, about Myrtilla cara–and just look at my type of all perfection, the Angel Raphael's left-hand in the great Perugino,–it will refresh you and contrast, ever more brightly and richly, with modern mud and pewter.—But– . . . . . . the idea of asking why a hand is so difficult! Why it's ever so much harder than even a foot–and for an *arm*–nobody ever could *paint a* girl's arm yet–from elbow to wrist.—It's not quite fair to show you these two *tries* of yours–but yet, the moral of them is that you must cure yourself of thinking so much of hair and hats and parasols–and attend *first*, (for some time to come) to toes–fingers–and wrists.

A birthday greeting for
John Ruskin, 1893

Kate's letters to Ruskin between 1885 and his death present us with intimate glimpses of her artistic and literary tastes; her hatred of change and the confusion of life; her discontent with her work and her determination to do better in the future; her love of space; her artistic methods; her views upon the Impressionist tendency of art; and last, but not in her eyes less important, extracts from Rover's biography.

Very few letters were preserved by Ruskin before 1887, and they are not of great interest. Here are excerpts from later ones that his executors were able to find:

In 1895 she writes:

Nov. 11, 1895.

I am still in a state of great perplexity as to what work to do and as to what to agree to about books. There is no Almanack this year. Now they want to do it again and I find it hard to decide if I will or not—partly because I do not make up my mind about what I want to do in other ways. But often when I feel like this I wait, and an inspiration comes.

Some beautiful picture or drawing will make me long to do something. The worst of it is, I ought always to do everything the moment it suggests itself, or very likely by the time I go to do it the spirit of it has vanished.

I do the technical part of painting so badly, and every one else seems to do it so well. I have no settled way of working—I am always trying this or that.

39, FROGNAL, 29 *Jan.* 1896.

Oh dear! Things *are so* beautiful and wonderful, you feel there must be another life where you will see more—hear move—and *know* more. All of it cannot die.

I hope you get out every day for nice walks. Though I do not wish time away I am glad this is February, the first spring month. I wonder what you read now.

Feb. 25, 1896.

I wonder if you ever see any illustrations of Aubrey Beardsley's and what do you think of them? I would like to know. A great many people are now what they call modern. When I state *my* likes and dislikes they tell me I am *not* modern, so I suppose I'm not—advanced. That is why, I suppose, I see some of the new pictures as looking so very funny. You must not like Leighton now, or Millais, and I don't know how much longer I'm to be allowed to like Burne-Jones. Oh dear! I believe I shall ever think a face should look like a face, and a beautiful arm like a beautiful arm—not that I can do it—the great pity I can't. Why, if I could, they should have *visions*. Sometimes I almost wish I were shut up by myself with nothing to do but to paint—only I'm so dependent on people's affection. I'm not lonely by myself but I want the people I like very much sometimes. I feel I shall not do anything of what I could wish in my life. Isn't it hard sometimes when you have felt the beauty of something in a certain way and have done it so and *no one* you show it to seems to see it at all. But I suppose if it is really a good thing you have done that, after years, some one does feel it, while if it is not worth finding out it goes into oblivion—so Time sifts it all out. Such is not my fate, for I unfortunately can only think of all the beautiful things and have not the skill to do them.

In 1896 she writes:

March 22.

You can go into a beautiful new country if you stand under a large apple tree and look up to the blue sky through the white flowers—to go to this scented land is an experience.

I suppose I went to it very young before I could really remember and that is why I have such a wild delight in cowslips and appleblossom—they always give me the same strange feeling of trying *to remember*, as if I had known them in a former world.

I always feel Wordsworth must have left that a little too—when he wrote the 'Intimations of Immortality'—I mean the trying to remember.

It's such a beautiful world, especially in the spring. It's a pity it's so sad also. I often reproach the plan of it. It seems as if some less painful and repulsive end could have been found for its poor helpless inhabitants—considering the wonderfulness of it all.—WELL, it isn't the least use troubling.

What a delight her letters were to him when ill-health made any written response impracticable may be gathered from Mrs. Severn's re-iterated announcements:

'The Professor is absorbed with delight in your letter.'— 'Your letters are always so interesting and a real pleasure to *him*.'—'How grateful I ever am for your *untiring goodness* to him. Your letters really are one of the *great* pleasures of his life.'—'Your lovely letter with the sweet little people look-ing from the ridge of the hill at the rising sun so delighted Di Pa. (Di Pa was Ruskin's pet name within his immediate family.) He looked at it long and lovingly and kept repeating "Beautiful! beautiful! beautiful!"' And when he was ill in 1897:—'Your letters (the only ones he at present has) he much enjoys.'

Still in 1896 Kate writes:

March 1896.

How funny it is, the different ways different people feel you ought to work! and people who, you feel, should know. One man said, 'Now, what

89

On a letter to Ruskin

24 November
1897.

39, FROGNAL,
HAMPSTEAD, N.W.

On a letter to Ruskin

I would like to see is all these things done *life size!*' Another comes back as if he had quite a weight on his mind to say he feels he must tell me how much he feels I ought to etch, so that my own original work was kept. Some one else wants me always to do small things; some one else, land-scapes,—so it goes on. The man with the donkey who tried to please every-body is nothing to it!

And again in July:

July 9, 1896.

I saw two little children in an omnibus yesterday—two little girls. I was so much taken with their faces—they had such small eyes but exactly the shape of some Italian ones. I seemed to know every line as I had seen it in carved Italian faces—it was so beautifully formed, all the eyelid round the eye. . . . I did long to ask their mother to let me draw them. I could have done them with such joy.

Aug. 13, 1896.

I have not had a nice book this week. I read George Fox, the Quaker, the other day. He was very wonderful, but some things they make a stand for seem hardly worth it, like keeping their hats on. But perhaps that is me in fault, for I don't think I am at all regulated by Forms; they don't ever feel to me to matter: I don't feel my life gets much shaped by them—but then perhaps it would be better for me if it did!

Oct. 21, 1896.

The colours are beautiful this year. Here, the Heath looks wonderful, it is all so brilliant—red orange, emerald green, Rossetti's green; it always makes me think of Rossetti. I see the colour he *tried* for, and how difficult it is! You can't think what colours to paint it with because it always looks so cold when it is done—not a bit like the real colour. I despair over grass, I can't do it! I don't know what it is; I don't know what blue to use—or what yellow. I'm so longing to try more body-colour. It's a curious thing

90

everybody runs it down—yet—all the great water-colour people (the modern ones) have used it—W. Hunt, Walker, Pinwell, Rossetti, Burne-Jones, Herkomer.

April 15, 1897.

Isn't it a funny thing I can't copy? All the morning I have been blundering over a baby's face from a little study. I can't do it a bit; it is odd. I can't get it a bit like the original. I put it in and take it out, and so it goes on getting worse and worse. And I wish I could do it so much but I never have been able, and it don't matter what it is—it is everything—the most trifling thing. I never do it well except direct from the object or my own mind, but I can't copy a flat thing—it really is curious. . . . .

The gentleman who has his nursery hung round with my drawings has seen those I did for you and is very much taken with them He wanted me to copy the two big ones, but I told him that was perfectly impossible. So I'm going to do him a procession later on. Also I should not like him to have drawings the same as yours.

April 22, 1897.

I am very fond of *Nicholas Nickleby.* No one has liked Dickens for so long, but I think I begin to see a little turn coming now. Of course in time it would be sure to come, but it is a certain fate to every one after a time, and then another thing sets in and they take their rank for ever. . . .

Kate writes of Millais (his *Ophelia* was one of her favorite pictures):

July 14, 1897.

There was a Millais—three Millais'—'The Huguenots,' 'The Gambler's Wife,' and 'The Blind Girl.' Every time I see any of the early Millais' I like them more and more, if possible. 'The Huguenots' is so wonderful, isn't it? Her face! it seems to move and quiver as you look at it—it is a divine picture. I do only wish he had not made the colour in the girl's sleeves yellow, or that yellow. Then the wall and the campanulas and nasturtiums—her hands and his!—

I know you do not always like Tadema, but there is one here I think you would like—both the painting and the subject, but very likely you have seen it. I never have before. It is called 'The Women of Amphissa.' Do you know it? Some women have gone on a pilgrimage and have strayed into an enemy's city and are taken care of and given food by the women of the city. The *food* is so wonderful. There is some honey in the comb, and cucumbers and figs and bread. There are two fair women who are marvels of painting.

Then there's a Holman Hunt—'The Boys Singing on May Morning,' (at Oxford)—but the reflections are so exaggerated it cuts it up too much. But

Bookplate for
Lady Victoria Herbert

well do I love the early one, 'The Two Gentlemen of Verona.' I have often seen this before and I love it. It really is so beautiful to see such pictures.

Then there's a Lewis—such painting, such colour! What a wonderful collection of men they were!

And what will this generation who run them down have to show? For them, *nothing* that I can see at present. There are two Turners, but by the time I got to those I was feeling too tired to stand. I fear I shan't go again for I think it closes to-day.

There, it is all pictures this time, but I feel so much better for seeing them. I always do, if I can see a beautiful thing.

Nov. 24, 1897.

What do you think I have been drawing to-day? I got so interested it has made me very tired. I am doing a band of little child angels each carrying a lily coming along a hilltop against a green (summer) sunset sky. May-trees are in flower, and they are (one or two of the angels) gathering daisies. The lilies are heavenly lilies, so it doesn't matter their being out at the same time as the May. I have not yet finished the starry sky, but I was constrained to do the angels.

In 1898 Kate writes of her admiration for the Pre-Raphaelites, Millais in particular:

Jan. 12, 1898.

I went yesterday afternoon to see the Millais' at the R. A. and I think them more wonderful than ever.

It is splendid the impression of beauty and power—as you first step into the rooms. Do you know well 'The Boyhood of Sir Walter Raleigh'? I think that boy's face is the most beautiful I have ever seen—it makes me cry to look at it. Its expression is so intensely wonderful—so is 'The Stowaway.'—But it is going from one masterpiece to another. Still there are some which do not appeal to me as much as others. The divine 'Ophelia' is there as divine as ever. People are making up to it. I have thought it the most wonderful picture ever since I first saw it.

Then there is the girl's face in 'Yes!'—full of the most beautiful feeling—like the Huguenot girl.—How he painted those children!—Angels of Beauty. He is really a marvel. . . . . .

I should like to have a sort of little packing case made that I could put drawings into and send backwards and forwards for you to see—sometimes —only perhaps you wouldn't like them If you would it would be rather nice—a very narrow flat box always ready.

I fear the exhibition won't be in the least successful; there seems to me to be very few pictures sell now—or a person is popular just for a little

92

time. And there's so much fad over art—if you like the new things they say you are modern. I say Art isn't modern: new or old in a way. It is like summer is summer—spicy is spicy, and Art is Art, for as long as the world is—isn't that true? However, they have woke up to the 'Ophelia' so I forgive them a good deal.

But I can't help feeling boiling over with rage when I read the criticisms in some of the papers—so utterly ignorant; and then people who don't know are guided by this. I daresay you will say, 'But what do the people who don't know matter?'—They don't—but it is depressing.

Jan. 27.

I have been to see the Rossettis again to-day for a little change, for I was too tired for anything. I like the small water-colours more and more. The colours are so wonderful. I feel I *do* such weak things and think strong ones, and it is dreadfully tiresome. I do want to do something nice—beautiful—like I feel—like I see in my mind, and there I am trammelled by technical short-comings. I will never begin a lot of things together again because then you can't do new ideas or try different ways of work, and I always could only do one thing at once. I live in the one thing and think about it, and it's like a real thing or place for the time. Even now, the moment I'm doing a new drawing the morning rushes by—I'm so happy, so interested, I only feel the tiredness when I can't go on because it is too late or too dark.

Later, we hear a note of discouragement:

May 27, 1898.

I wish I did not have to make any money. I would like to work very hard but in a different way so that I was more free to do what I liked, and it is so difficult now I am no longer at all the fashion. I say fashion, for that is the right word, that is all it is to a great many people.

On a letter to Ruskin

Oct. 26, 1898.

How curiously days come back to you, or rather, live for ever in your life —never go out of it, as if the impression was so great it could never go away again. I could tell you so many such. One is often present I think I must tell that one now. Go and stand in a shady lane—at least, a wide country road—with high hedges, and wide grassy places at the sides. The hedges are all hawthorns blossoming; in the grass grow great patches of speedwell, stitchwort, and daisies. You look through gates into fields full of buttercups, and the whole of it is filled with sunlight. For I said it was shady only because the hedges were high. Now do you see my little picture, and me a little dark girl in a pink frock and hat, looking about at things a good deal, and thoughts filled up with such wonderful things—everything seeming wonderful, and life to go on for ever just as it was. What a beautiful long time a day was! Filled with time—

Nov. 7, 1898.

I am reading a strange French Play. I should like to see it acted—*Cyrano de Bergerac.* I feel it would be very taking when played.

It is so strange all the great things are a sacrifice. The thing that appeals supremely seems to me always that. Yet how sad it should be, for to the one it means desolation. It is a strange world this. How queer it all is, isn't it? living at all—and our motives and things matter, and liking beautiful things, and the while really not knowing anthing about the Vital Part of it—the Before and the After.

And undated letters, but of this period:

I have just heard from Joanie that you spent your day in the drawing-room yesterday—so you would see the Burne-Jones' and the Hunts. How slowly the Hunts have dawned on me—but it is a comfort *they have dawned,* isn't it? ? ? ? Ah, you say, WHAT a benighted being, what a little Heathen! to have been so long.

What a fuss there has been about Sir Herbert Kitchener!—I like it.— He must have felt it was very nice for people to be so glad. I like a great deal made of people who do things.

In the same strain she had written of another hero to Miss Dickinson the year before:—

I'm very much impressed by Lord Roberts' Indian book. I met him many years ago at a children's party at Lady Jeune's. She told us we were rival attractions and the little Princes and Princesses couldn't make up their minds which of us they wanted to see most.

94

On a letter to Ruskin

He *was brave*—so were the others; they were a brave and noble lot. It seems too wonderful as you read to think how people can be like that, going to certain death—to the suffering of anguish. It feels to me too much to take—too much to accept—but it's beautiful.

Jan. 3, 1899.

I'm not doing drawings that at all interest me just now. They are just single figures of children which I always spoil by the backgrounds. I never can put a background into a painting of a single figure, while in a drawing there isn't the least difficulty. Perhaps I don't trouble about the reality in the drawing. I put things just where I want them, not, possibly, as they ought to go. And that seems to me the difficulty of full-length portraits. It is all quite easy with just a head or half length. It is funny the background should be the difficulty. The most modern way is to have a highly done-out background and a figure lost in mist, but I don't see this. So I can't take refuge there.

Miss Greenaway's difficulty with backgrounds is that shared by every artist, more or less. G. F. Watts, R.A., used to quote Rubens, who said that 'the man who can paint a background can paint a portrait.'

Jan. 11, 1899.

What dismal books people do write! I have just been reading a story by Hardy called *The Woodlanders*, so spoilt by coarseness and unnaturalness. I say spoilt by this, for there are parts of it so beautiful—all the descriptions of the country and the cider-making—it is all so well described you really feel there. The end of the book is simply *Hateful*. I hated to think his mind *could* make it end so. Did you ever read any of his books? so many people now seem to me to make things unnatural—it is a curious thing to think so, but I'm sure it is that they do—and the natural is so much greater. They like things odd—eccentric.

95

I went to see the Burne-Jones drawings yesterday. They are very lovely. There are two or three I would like to have, but indeed there is not one I would not, but there are two or three I would love to possess—a procession with such lovely young girls in it. The studies for the pictures are so beautiful—the chalk and pencil drawings. He draws such beautiful faces; and I like his later drawings often better than his earlier ones. He certainly had not gone off, except perhaps in colour—but that was a phase. He had grown to like colder colour, brown and cold grey, which I did not always like, preferring the beautiful colouring of the 'Chant d'Amour' and 'Venus Vinctrix.' But then, I like colour so much. Well, the *world is* Coloured, so are people. I see colour higher than things uncoloured for that reason.

May 17, 1899.

I am improving now in my oil-painting. I begin to make the flesh look like flesh and no longer white and chalky. I like doing it so much and if only the models would not talk so much!—But how they talk! and if you stop them talking they gape and make such ugly faces! Some one was telling me that Sir Joshua Reynolds, to stop his sitters' talking, had a glass put up so that they could see him working. I think of adopting that plan. You can't think what you are doing while you have to listen. I can't see why they want to talk so and never think. How funny it would be to have a mind that never liked to be alone with its own thoughts—very dreadful I should find it. I get to feel very tired and miserable if I can't have any time to be quiet in.

May 31, 1899.

You can't think how funny it is—but finding the power of oil-painting now, my curious mind is wishing to see, and seeing, all subjects large; it seems as if my long-ago and ever-constant wish—to paint a life-size hedge— might now be realised. What a divine thing to do! A life-sized girl in the front and then the large foxgloves and wild roses, and strawberries on the ground. I should be lost in my picture. I should have to have a stool that moved up and carried me about over my picture. All the same I should not wonder if I *do* do a life-size thing! Perhaps I have hopes of the capacity oil paint that won't be realised, but it is nice to get a medium to work in that does what ou want more at once. I don't like small oil things half as much as water-colours—but I do lose the *go* of things in water-colours.

June 7, 1899.

I went to the Tate Gallery the other afternoon, and somehow I didn't like it—much. It is a beautiful Gallery, but somehow tomb-like—and my dearest-loved of English pictures, Millais' 'Ophelia,' doesn't look its best

"Rover," for ten years Kate
Greenaway's faithful companion.

there. Now I feel this picture ought to have a gallery that suits it exactly!
but perhaps some other time I may go and like it ever so much. As it was,
I grieve to say, the entrance was what I liked best, going out and coming
in. There's the beautiful river and the boats and the opposite shore of
wharves and buildings.

July 25, 1899.

Dear Rover's pride has had a fall. There are two swans have come to
live on the White Stone pond, and Rover goes and swims there on his
way home. Johnny said he could see the people round the pond laughing,
and when he got up to it there was Rover swimming about as if the pond
belonged to him, while the swans who thought it belonged to them were
fluttering their wings and craning their necks. Rover still remained unconcerned and imperturbable, when one of the swans took hold of his tail
and pulled it! This did vanquish Rover, who left the pond hurriedly amidst
the derisive laughter of the bystanders.

He has some nice friendly swans on the other pond who swim up and
down with him. I suppose he thought all swans were alike. I am curious
to know if he goes in to-day. . . . . . Dear Rover stood firm and did go in.
Johnny saw him quite unconcerned swimming about with the swans flap-
ping about at the back. Now don't you think this was much to his credit?
I only hope they won't peck him!

In Kate Greenaway's diary of January 20, 1900, appeared the following entry:—

'Mr. Ruskin died today at 2:30 in the afternoon from influenza.'

This chapter may fitly be brought to a close by the following handsome defence of Ruskin, inspired by a conversation with Miss Violet
Dickinson, and written twelve months before the last letter.

Nov. 2, 1896.

I have been thinking very much about what you said, of the way people talk against him in Venice—I hope you will try a little not to quite believe it all. For believe me it is sure not to be all true, and even if he has been very inaccurate the world owes him so much that one may well and justly (I think) forget his faults.

The world *is* very ungrateful like all nature is, and takes all the good it can get and then flings the giver of it away. That is our way and it is a cruel one. And there's another reason also—a reason that once I used not to believe in—but I do now, and that is that so many of the second-rate authors and artists seem to have a most bitter jealousy of the great ones. It is very curious to me but they do. They love to find a fault. Look how delighted they were to think Carlyle was unkind to Mrs. Carlyle, while really I suppose he never was. When Mr. du Maurier died the other day such unfair notices of both his books and drawings!—I feel red-hot angry at lots of the things said about the big ones, and we ought to be so grateful to them instead for what they make the world for us. Nearly always the criticisms are from the lesser man on the great one. How should he know? —If he did he would be the great one, but he isn't and can't be, and nothing shows more how little and below he is. More than that, he can't reverence and venerate those wonderful souls who shower down so freely for everybody the greatness that is in them. I feel I can say all this to you for you *are* a feeling soul, and I know you'll go with me. Not that I mean for one moment that it is right not to be accurate, and I know in Mr. Ruskin's case he is too ready to believe all he hears, but I think it should be forgiven—that the beautiful things he tells you—and the new life of Art you enter into—compensate.

Never shall I forget what I felt in reading *Fors Clavigera* for the first time, and it was the first book of his I had ever read. I longed for each evening to come that I might lose myself in that new wonderful world.

A CENTURY OF
KATE GREENAWAY

HE WORLD over the name of Kate Greenaway holds the mystery and magic of a familiar fairy tale in many a household and in those libraries and schools and bookshops where her picture books have been cherished and freshly explored by one generation after another.

Once in a hundred years I like to think the golden key to the kingdom of childhood unlocks the door for a rare creative spirit, who, in pictures or words, records what is seen and felt with a truth and beauty that defy time and space.

It was a purely visionary world that William Blake recorded for the eighteenth century in his *Songs of Innocence*. It was a very human world in which real children dance and play and sing in sunlit streets and gardens or beside the sea that Kate Greenaway recorded for the nineteenth century in *Under the Window* and *Marigold Garden*.

Clear memory of the wonder of her own happy childhood in country and city was behind these essentially English scenes. It is said that "K. G.", as she was familiarly known in her own time, never forgot the colour or form of anything she had looked upon in childhood. She seems to have been born with the rare sense of colour and design which has distinguished her work as the pioneer among picture books of a new order.

Twenty years after the publication of *Under the Window*, hailed in France, Germany, Holland, Belgium, and the United States, almost as soon as in England, for its originality and truth to child life, Kate Greenaway wrote in a letter to Ruskin with whom she had corresponded during all that time:

"There are not any very good children's books about just now that I have seen. The rage for copying mine seems over, so I suppose someone will soon step to the front with something new. Children often don't care a bit about the books people think they will and I think they often like grown-up books—at any rate I did. From Kenny Meadows' pictures to Shakespeare I learnt all the plays when I was very young indeed. It is curious how much the pictures can tell you—like the plays without words. I suppose I asked a good deal about them and was told and read little bits. I never remember when I didn't know what each play was about."

Kate Greenaway looked with her own eyes at the children she had seen in garden, village or farm, in London streets or beside the sea, and wrote verses to accompany them without apparently realizing that she was making a notable picture book. She had been told by Mr. William Marcus Ward for whose house she had designed Christmas cards and valentines that her verses were "rubbish and without any poetic feeling," but although she unhesitatingly accepted Mr. Ward's expert opinion on her drawings and destroyed those he considered bad she reserved the right to set down her thoughts in her own way, and continued to do so until she had made a collection of fifty or more. These she took to Edmund Evans, the colour printer, who had published the toy-books of Walter Crane and was beginning to publish those of Caldecott.

Mr. Evans had known John Greenaway, the father of Kate, a well-known wood-engraver and draughtsman of the time who had been assistant engraver to Ebenezer Landells, the originator of *Punch*, to whom Mr. Evans was apprenticed as a boy.

"I was fascinated with the originals of the drawings and the ideas of the verses," he said, "so I at once purchased them and determined to reproduce them in a small volume. The title, *Under the Window*, was selected afterwards from one of the first lines. At the suggestion of George Routledge & Sons I took the drawings and verses to Frederick Locker, the author of *London Lyrics*. . . . Locker was very much taken with the drawings and verses and showed them to Mrs. Locker with quite a gusto; he asked me many questions about her and was evidently interested in what I told him of her. I do not think he did anything to improve the verses nor did K. G. herself. . . .

"After I had engraved the blocks and colour blocks I printed the first edition of 20,000 volumes and was ridiculed by the publishers for risking such a large edition of a six-shilling book; but the edition sold before I could reprint another edition; in the meantime copies were sold at a premium. Reprinting kept on until 70,000 was reached." French and German editions brought the numbers up to 100,000 copies or more. *Under the Window* was published in 1878.

Everything about *Under the Window* was fresh and different from any picture book that had been seen before—the lovely cover design, the pictorial title-page, the unique table of contents, reproducing in miniature and in colour the figures from each complete drawing in the book.

No one who had known the book in childhood seems to have forgotten its form or any of its pictures. And what a variety of activities and sheer nonsense appear ranging from the Five Little Sisters standing in a row in their big hats with their muffs, the supercilious Prince Finikin sipping tea with his mamma in the garden of his castle, the children just let out of school, the Proud Girl that struts about to the sheer loveliness of the Maying Party with their baskets of wildflowers and flowering branches.

"Children like something that excites their imagination—a very real thing mixed up with a great unreality like Bluebeard," Kate Greenaway wrote in a letter regarding an exhibition of pictures for children that was to be held at the Fine Art Society in December 1899. She expresses doubt that children will appreciate the exhibition. "I often notice that they don't at all care for what grown-up people think they will," and recalls how thrilled she used to be by "Sister Ann, Sister Ann!" done in the agonized voice of Bluebeard's wife. "I could hardly breathe when the stains would not come off the key."

"Those wonderful little books they used to sell in coloured covers, a penny and a half-penny each. They were all deeply fascinating but I think I liked best *The Sleeping Beauty in the Wood, Cinderella* and *Beauty and the Beast*. It would be curious to do a book of them from one's remembrance of them in one's early thoughts. I know my Bluebeard people were not dressed as Turks then."

Such observations indicate how keenly aware Kate Greenaway was of the changing patterns in the field of art in the 1890's. And how firmly rooted in childhood as an unchanging element in human life was her way of seeing and recording what she felt when she looked.

I visited the children's rooms of several branches of the New York Public Library, where I learned at first hand that in circulation for reading at home, as well as in the reading-rooms in the Library, Kate Greenaway holds a place of her own.

That boys, as well as girls, enjoy Kate Greenaway's pictures and frequently join the groups to which the verses are being read I was told at each of the children's rooms I visited. This did not surprise me for boys care quite as much about flowers and gardens and often bring a keener appreciation for the background of a picture than do girls.

ANNE CARROLL MOORE

UNDER THE WINDOW

PICTVRES & RHYMES
for Children

by

KATE GREENAWAY

Partial text and illustrations

UNDER THE
WINDOW

UNDER the window is my garden,
　　Where sweet, sweet flowers grow;
And in the pear-tree dwells a robin,
　　The dearest bird I know.

Tho' I peep out betimes in the morning,
　　Still the flowers are up the first;
Then I try and talk to the robin,
　　And perhaps he'd chat—if he durst

KG

You see, merry Phillis, that dear little maid,
    Has invited Belinda to tea;
Her nice little garden is shaded by trees—
    What pleasanter place could there be?

There's a cake full of plums, there are strawberries too,
    And the table is set on the green;
I'm fond of a carpet all daisies and grass—
    Could a prettier picture be seen?

A blackbird (yes, blackbirds delight in warm weather,)
    Is flitting from yonder high spray;
He sees the two little ones talking together—
    No wonder the blackbird is gay!

K.C

SCHOOL is over,
  Oh, what fun !
Lessons finished,
  Play begun.
Who'll run fastest,
  You or I ?
Who'll laugh loudest ?
  Let us try.

K.G.

As I was walking up the street,
   The steeple bells were ringing ;
As I sat down at Mary's feet,
   The sweet, sweet birds were singing

As I walked far into the world,
   I met a little fairy ;
She plucked this flower, and, as it's sweet,
   I've brought it home to Mary.

FIVE little sisters walking in a row ;
Now, isn't that the best way for little girls to go ?
Each had a round hat, each had a muff,
And each had a new pelisse of soft green stuff.

Five little marigolds standing in a row ;
Now, isn't that the best way for marigolds to grow ?
Each with a green stalk, and all the five had got
A bright yellow flower, and a new red pot.

You are going out to tea to-day,
　So mind how you behave;
Let all accounts I have of you
　Be pleasant ones, I crave.

Don't spill your tea, or gnaw your bread,
　And don't tease one another;
And Tommy mustn't talk too much,
　Or quarrel with his brother.

Say "If you please," and "Thank you, Nurse:"
　Come home at eight o'clock;
And, Fanny, pray be careful that
　You do not tear your frock.

Now, mind your manners, children five,
　Attend to what I say;
And then, perhaps, I'll let you go
　Again another day.

Up you go, shuttlecocks, ever so high!
Why come you down again, shuttlecocks—why?
When you have got so far, why do you fall?
Where all are high, which is highest of all?

HIGGLEDY, piggledy ! see how they run !
Hopperty, popperty ! what is the fun ?
Has the sun or the moon tumbled into the sea ?
What is the matter, now ?   Pray tell it me !

Higgledy, piggledy ! how can I tell ?
Hopperty, popperty ! hark to the bell !
The rats and the mice even scamper away :
Who can say what may not happen to-day ?

KG

THE boat sails away, like a bird on the wing,
And the little boys dance on the sands in a ring.
The wind may fall, or the wind may rise—
You are foolish to go ; you will stay if you're wise.
The little boys dance, and the little girls run :
If it's bad to have money, it's worse to have none.

K G

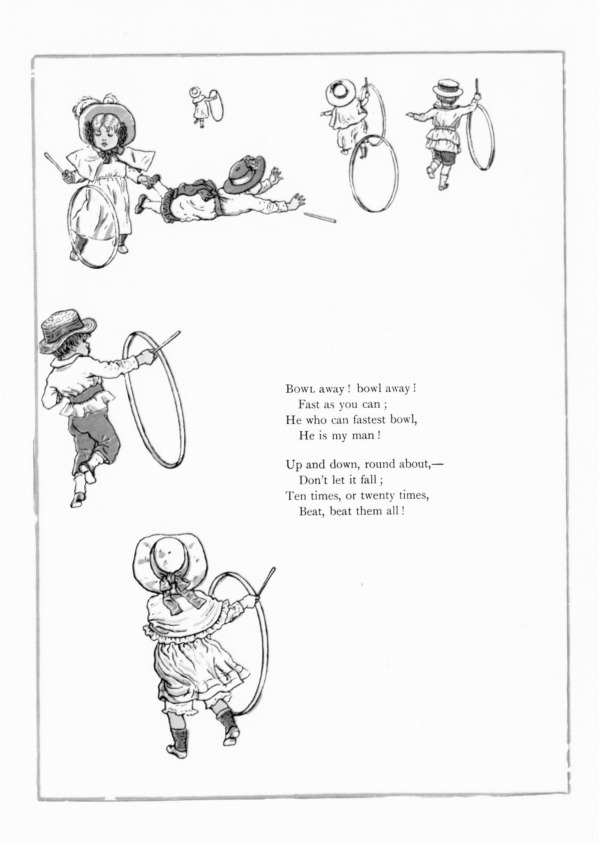

Bowl away! bowl away!
　Fast as you can;
He who can fastest bowl,
　He is my man!

Up and down, round about,—
　Don't let it fall;
Ten times, or twenty times,
　Beat, beat them all!

YES, it is sad of them—
 Shocking to me;
Bad—yes, it's bad of them—
 Bad of all three.

Warnings they've had from me.
 Still I repeat them—
Cold is the water—the
 Fishes will eat them.

Yet they will row about,
 'Tho' I say "Fie!" to them;
Fathers may scold at it,
 Mothers may cry to them.

K.G.

WHAT is Tommy running for,
   Running for,
   Running for?
What is Tommy running for,
  On this fine day?

Jimmy will run after Tommy,
   After Tommy,
   After Tommy;
That's what Tommy's running for,
  On this fine day.

A BUTCHER's boy met a baker's boy
  (It was all of a summer day):
Said the butcher's boy to the baker's boy,
  "Will you please to walk my way?"

Said the butcher's boy to the baker's boy,
  "My trade's the best in town,"
"If you dare say that," said the baker's boy,
  "I shall have to knock you down!"

Said the butcher's boy to the baker's boy,
  "That's a wicked thing to do;
And I think, before you've knocked me down,
  The cook will blow up *you!*"

The twelve Miss Pelicoes,
    Of course, to school were sent;
Their parents wished them to excel
    In each accomplishment.

The twelve Miss Pelicoes
    Played music—*Fal-lal-la!*
Which consequently made them all
    The pride of their papa.

The twelve Miss Pelicoes
    Learnt dancing and the globes;
Which proves that they were wise, and had
    That patience which was Job's.

THE twelve Miss Pelicoes
    Were twelve sweet little girls;
Some wore their hair in pigtail plaits,
    And some of them wore curls.

The twelve Miss Pelicoes
    Had dinner every day;—
A not uncommon thing at all,
    You probably will say.

The twelve Miss Pelicoes
    Went sometimes for a walk;
It also is a well-known fact
    That all of them could talk.

The twelve Miss Pelicoes
    Were always most polite—
Said "If you please," and "Many thanks,"
    "Good morning," and "Good night."

The twelve Miss Pelicoes
    You plainly see, were taught
To do the things they didn't like,
    Which means, the things they ought.

Now, fare ye well, Miss Pelicoes,
    I wish ye a good day;—
About these twelve Miss Pelicoes
    I've nothing more to say.

My house is red—a little house,
  A happy child am I,
I laugh and play the livelong day
  I hardly ever cry.

I have a tree, a green, green tree.
  To shade me from the sun;
And under it I often sit,
  When all my work is done.

My little basket I will take,
  And trip into the town;
When next I'm there I'll buy some cake,
  And spend my bright half-crown.

K.G

Prince Finikin and his mamma
    Sat sipping their bohea;
"Good gracious!" said his Highness, "why,
    What girl is this I see?

"Most certainly it cannot be
    A native of our town;
And he turned him round to his mamma,
    Who set her teacup down

But Dolly simply looked at them,
    She did not speak a word;
"She has no voice!" said Finikin;
    "It's really quite absurd."

Then Finikin's mamma observed,
    "Dear Prince, it seems to me,
She looks as if she'd like to drink
    A cup of my bohea."

So Finikin poured out her tea,
    And gave her currant-pie;
Then Finikin said, "Dear mamma,
    What a kind Prince am I!"

THREE little girls were sitting on a rail,
    Sitting on a rail,
    Sitting on a rail ;
Three little girls were sitting on a rail,
  On a fine hot day in September.

What did they talk about that fine day,
    That fine day,
    That fine day ?
What did they talk about that fine day,—
  That fine hot day in September ?

The crows and the corn they talked about,
    Talked about,
    Talked about ;
But nobody knows what was said by the crows,
  On that fine hot day in September.

RING the bells—ring!
Hip, hurrah for the King!
The dunce fell into the pool, oh!
The dunce was going to school, oh!
The groom and the cook
Fished him out with a hook,
And he piped his eye like a fool, oh!

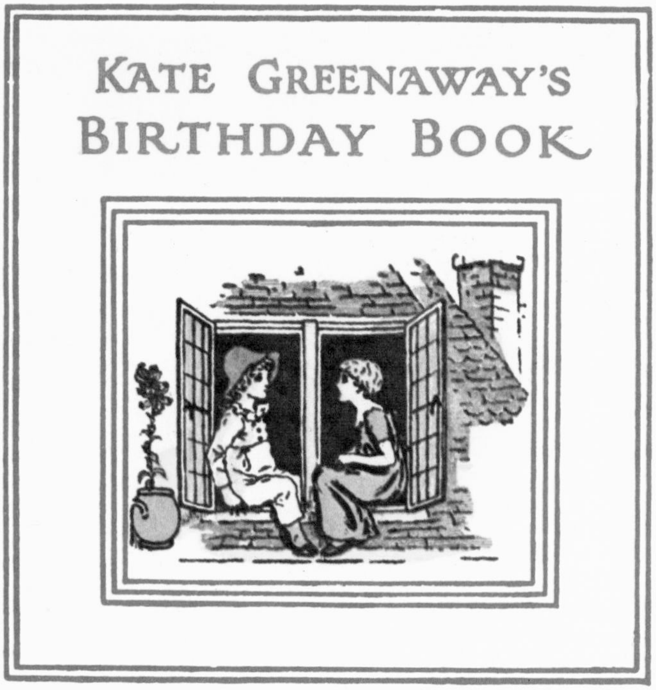
KATE GREENAWAY'S
BIRTHDAY BOOK

Kate Greenaway's
BIRTHDAY BOOK

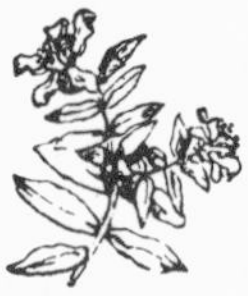

KATE GREENAWAY'S
BIRTHDAY BOOK

With verses by
MRS SALE BARKER

Partial text and illustrations

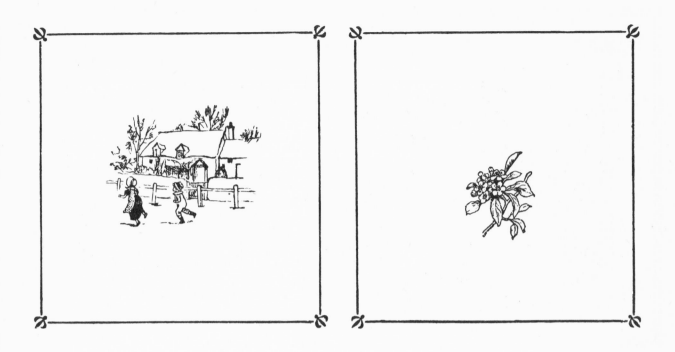

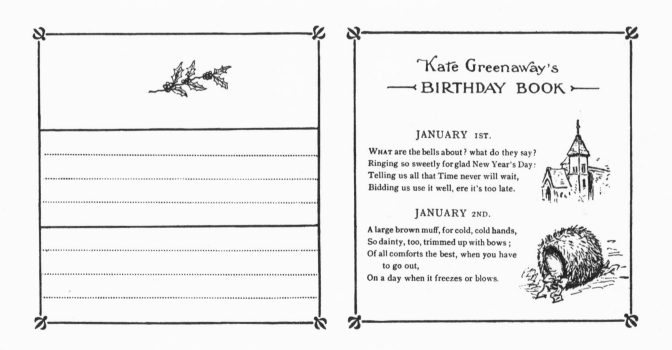

Kate Greenaway's
⤙ BIRTHDAY BOOK ⤚

JANUARY 1ST.

WHAT are the bells about? what do they say?
Ringing so sweetly for glad New Year's Day:
Telling us all that Time never will wait,
Bidding us use it well, ere it's too late.

JANUARY 2ND.

A large brown muff, for cold, cold hands,
So dainty, too, trimmed up with bows;
Of all comforts the best, when you have
    to go out,
On a day when it freezes or blows.

JANUARY 6TH.

So bright, so fresh, so delightfully nice,
To skim along on the hard smooth ice!
What fun to fly on your skates away,
Skating so gaily the whole of the day!

JANUARY 7TH.

Old Mrs. Big-bonnet, little Miss Wee,
Out for an airing, as you may see;
Chatter and chatter, and pleasantly talk,
Enjoying together their nice winter's walk.

JANUARY 8TH.

Who wouldn't go to a Fancy Ball?
High-heeled shoes to make us tall;
Ribbons, and laces, and powdered head,
And then to dance a minuet led.

FEBRUARY 5TH

A nice new broom, to sweep away,
And keep the floor so clean;
The crumbs and dust all disappear,
There's not one to be seen.

FEBRUARY 6TH.

The wind, determined to have some fun,
Blew an old woman to make her run;
The old woman trotted along with a will,
But stopped at last, when she got to a hill.

FEBRUARY 7TH.

A kite, one day, flew up in the sky,
To try and reach the sun;
He failed, and he fell with a broken string,
And sighed, " It can't be done ! "

MARCH 24TH.

The wind blew hard, the wind blew strong,
And blew Lucinda fast along;
At last it blew her up in the air,
Now, has she come down, or is she still there?

MARCH 25TH.

Ah! sweet primrose, you are come,
　To tell us of the Spring:
The hedge-rows bloom, the woods are green,
　And now the birdies sing.

MARCH 26TH.

Little Patty is delighted,
　What, do you think, about
All the flowers are shooting up
And all the buds are out.

APRIL 11TH.

Birdie, dear birdie, oh, whence do you come?
　Now say, do you bring any news?
Has mother come back from London town,
　And has she not brought me new shoes?

APRIL 12TH.

What's in the basket, the basket?
　What is there, great or small?
Perhaps plum buns and gingerbread,
　Perhaps there's none at all.

APRIL 13TH.

Cowslips, cowslips, fresh and sweet,
　And very, very dear!
I look at you, and then go back—
　Oh, many a long, long year!

MAY 11TH.

"Paddy, oh Paddy, now where do you go,
Stepping an Irish jig, dancing just so?."
"Oh, shure I'm off, then, to Dublin town,
To buy wife and children aich a new gown."

MAY 12TH.

Blossoms pink, and blossoms white,
    Flowering in May;
Sweet and bright, they bloom so fair,
    And all the world is gay.

MAY 13TH.

Such a big bonnet, a basket as big!
Is she going to market to buy a small pig?
When she comes back, it will be a fine joke,
A pig in a basket. a child in a poke.

JULY 4TH

I lie beside the running stream,
And watch the clouds, and rest, and dream:
A jug with water by me stands,
Which I have filled with my own hands.

JULY 5TH.

Sitting on the wall!
It is not safe at all.
Come, come, get down, I say;
You can't sit there all day.

JULY 6TH.

How I love the field flowers,
    Blooming bright and gay!
How I love the green, green fields,
    To wander there all day!

AUGUST 15TH.

This damsel seems extremely proud,
  Her nose so high in air;
I really don't think much of her,
  Such pride I cannot bear.

AUGUST 16TH.

What have you there, you dear little girl?
  What have you there, now tell?
Are they good, good things, you will have for tea;
  Or things that you want to sell?

AUGUST 17TH.

Out in the garden Miss Peachblossom ran,
A hat on her head, in her hand a great fan;
"I smell the sweet flowers—a bird past me flies;
Good-bye, pretty garden!" and back she then hies.

SEPTEMBER 20TH.

One large apple! is it for me?
Who has picked it off the tree?
We'll have it peeled, and put in a pie,
And then we'll eat it, you and I.

SEPTEMBER 21ST.

I should think it very hard,
  And also rather sad,
To dance alone, with so much grace
  Indeed, it is too bad.

SEPTEMBER 22ND.

Polly has got a new Bow-wow,
  Polly is merry and gay;
Polly thinks the whole world bright,
  And this the happiest day.

OCTOBER 2ND.

This boy is going to sail his boat,
  In a certain pond so round;
The pond is in Kensington Gardens—
  You know it, I'll be bound.

OCTOBER 3RD.

Oh, here we are in the country!
  Look at this bowl of cream!
And, you will see, five-o'clock tea
Delightful now will seem.

OCTOBER 4TH.

Out of the sweet, sweet flowers
  This funny goblin sprang;
And all the roses shook their heads,
  And all the blue-bells rang.

NOVEMBER 13TH.

"I must go to the stables,
  I must hie to the barn;
I must look to the horses,
  And see they come to no harm."

NOVEMBER 14TH.

"Oh, buy my oranges! buy, I pray!
  I'm very—very poor;
You're warm and happy in your homes,
  I stand cold at the door."

NOVEMBER 15TH.

A very old goblin lives in this tower,
  He eats nothing but mustard and batter;
And why should he choose such very odd fare?
  I will tell you—he's mad as a hatter.

NOVEMBER 19TH.

How cold she must be, that poor little mite;
   Look at her little bare arm;
I hope that Jack Frost won't give her a bite,
   That the weather will not do her harm.

NOVEMBER 20TH.

Strike the tree, woodman,
   Strike, strike away!
Strike, strike the grand old tree,
   Strike while you may!

NOVEMBER 21ST.

A lady went a-walking,
   She was so fair, so fair!
Alas! it is a picture,
   She is not really there.

DECEMBER 25TH.

Christmas! Hear the joy-bells ringing,
Glad hymns in the churches singing;
Of His mercy, of His power,
And the gifts good angels shower!

DECEMBER 26TH.

Why does she wear a steeple stuck upon her head?
This is a mediæval dress, so I've heard it said;
Why has she got a battledore and shuttlecock in
   hand?
To tell the truth, this lady I cannot understand.

DECEMBER 27TH.

A person once said "I will run;
You can have no idea of the fun
   Of running so fast
   That you drop down at last,
And feel that you're utterly done."

DECEMBER 31ST

This old woman takes a fly,
To sweep the cobwebs off the sky.
She says, "As I'm going up so high,
I wish the Old Year, and you all, Good-bye."

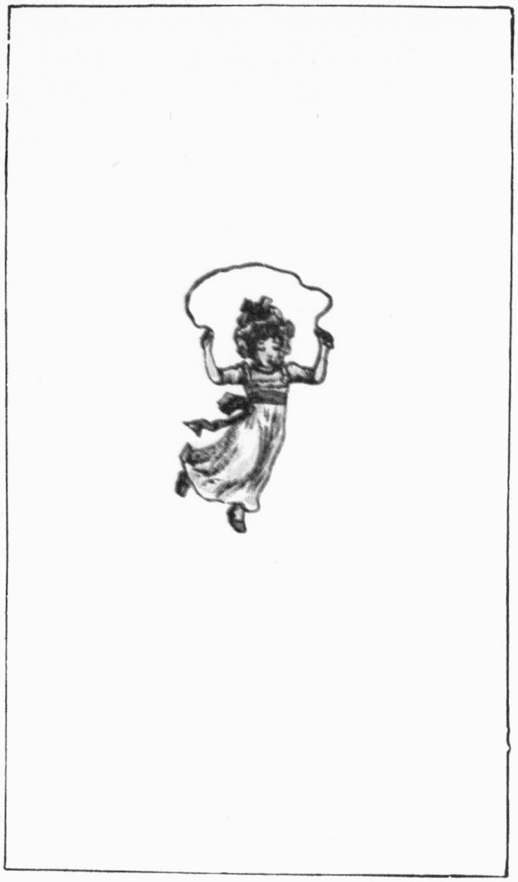

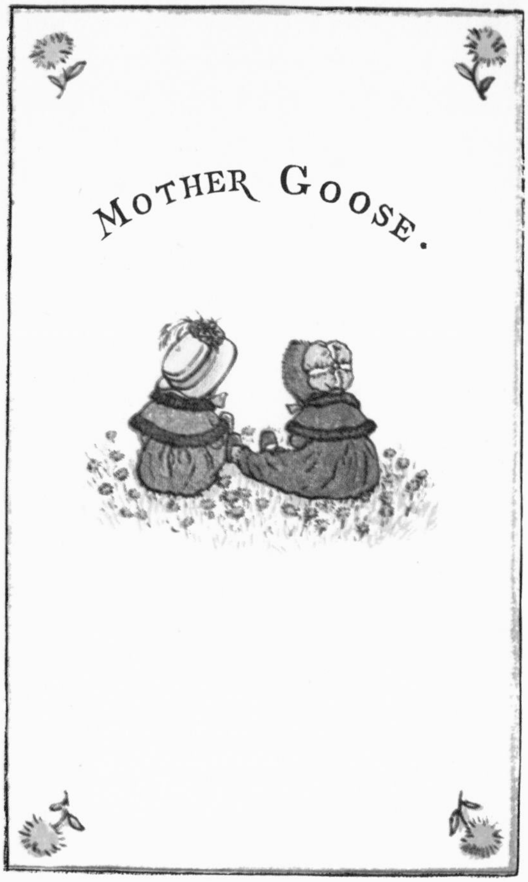

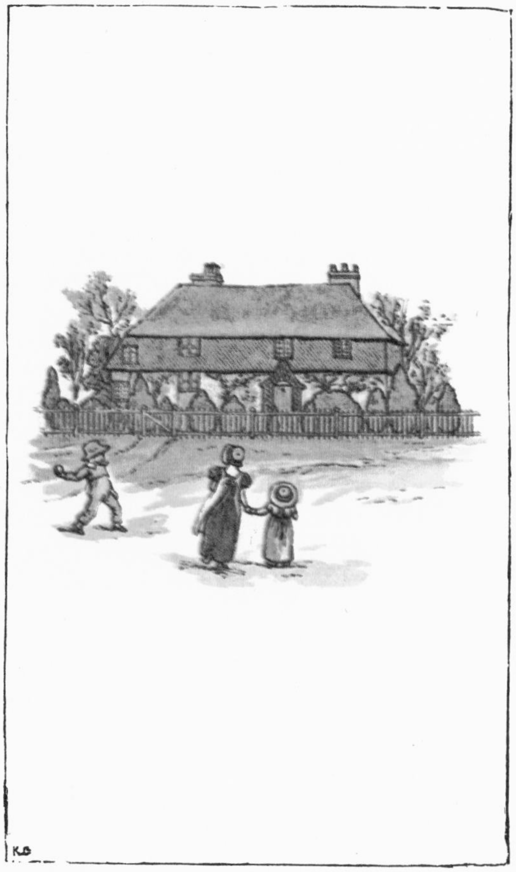

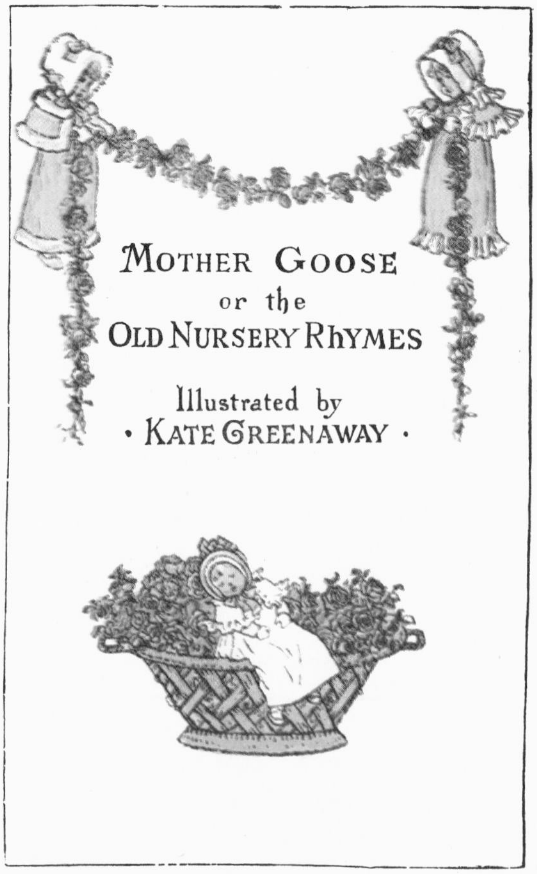

Partial text and illustrations

Rock-a-bye baby,
Thy cradle is green;
Father's a nobleman,
Mother's a queen.
And Betty's a lady,
And wears a gold ring;
And Johnny's a drummer,
And drums for the king.

Little lad, little lad,
Where wast thou born?
Far off in Lancashire,
Under a thorn;
Where they sup sour milk
From a ram's horn.

There was an old woman
Lived under a hill ;
And if she's not gone,
She lives there still.

Elsie Marley has grown so fine,
She won't get up to serve the swine ,
But lies in bed till eight or nine.
And surely she does take her time.

Johnny shall have a new bonnet,
And Johnny shall go to the fair ;
And Johnny shall have a blue ribbon,
To tie up his bonny brown hair.

Jack and Jill
Went up the hill,
To fetch a pail of water ;
Jack fell down
And broke his crown,
And Jill came tumbling after.

Girls and boys come out to play,
The moon it shines as bright as day;
Leave your supper, and leave your sleep,
And come to your playmates in the street;
Come with a whoop, come with a call,
Come with a good will, or come not at all;
Up the ladder and down the wall,
A halfpenny loaf will serve us all.

Little Betty Blue,
Lost her holiday shoe.
What will poor Betty do?
Why, give her another,
To match the other,
And then she will walk in two.

Billy boy blue, come blow me your horn,
The sheep's in the meadow, the cow's
    in the corn;
Is that the way you mind your sheep,
Under the haycock fast asleep!

Here am I, little jumping Joan,
When nobody's with me,
I'm always alone.

Ride a cock-horse,
To Banbury-cross,
To see little Johnny
Get on a white horse.

Humpty Dumpty sat on a wall,
Humpty Dumpty had a great fall.

Tom, Tom, the piper's son,
He learnt to play when he was young,
He with his pipe made such a noise,
That he pleased all the girls and boys.

Ring-a-ring-a-roses,
A pocket full of posies;
Hush! hush! hush! hush!
We're all tumbled down.

Goosey, goosey, gander,
Where shall I wander?
Up stairs, down stairs,
And in my lady's chamber:
There I met an old man,
Who would not say his prayers;
Take him by the left leg,
Throw him down the stairs.

Polly put the kettle on,
Polly put the kettle on,
Polly put the kettle on,
We'll all have tea.
Sukey take it off again,
Sukey take it off again,
Sukey take it off again,
They're all gone away.

ENGRAVED AND PRINTED BY
EDMUND EVANS, LTD.
ROSE PLACE, GLOBE ROAD,
LONDON, E.

Endpaper from *A Day in a Child's Life*

A
DAY IN A CHILD'S LIFE.

Complete text and illustrations

A DAY IN A CHILD'S LIFE

ILLUSTRATED BY

KATE GREENAWAY

MUSIC BY MYLES B. FOSTER

(Late Organist of the Foundling Hospital.)

Waking . . . . A. Marrvat.

The Lesson . . . Anon.

Playtime . . . . W. Hamilton.

Grace before Meals . Herrick.

Song of a Doll . . Charles Kingsley.

A Romp . . M. B. Foster.

Tired . . . Somerville Gibney.

Child's Prayer M. L. Duncan.

Sleeping . . Anon

WAKING.

Brightly.

1. Wake up! the sun is shi-ning Up-on the win-dow-pane, And hark! the noi-sy spar-rows Are wide a-wake a-gain; Each lit-tle bud and blos-som Has lift-ed up its head To

greet the pleasant sunshine, While you are still in bed!

The sun himself has risen
　To call them, long ago ;
And he has tried to wake you
　This last half-hour, you know.

The merry little sunbeams
　Have travelled—oh, so far !
Have crept between the shutters,
　In spite of bolt and bar.

'Twas time, indeed, to wake you,
　At last they seemed to think ;
And shot their golden arrows
　Through every hole and chink.

And when the door was opened,
　And Mary came at last.
Your eyes were almost blinded,
　They fell so thick and fast.

Then wake, and, like the flowers,
　Lift up each sleepy head ;
It is too bright a morning
　To waste it all in bed.

No. 2.

THE LESSON.

In slow mazurka time.

1. 2.} A B C D E F G H I J K L M N O P Q R S T U V

PED.   *   PED.   *   *simile.*

W   X   Y   Z..........

1. Let - ters twen - ty - six you see In this Al - pha - bet to be;
2. Let - ters twen - ty - six we see In this Al - pha - bet to be;

Children to repeat in Chorus to words of verse 2.

Try and sing them all to me, And then your les son's said.
We have sung them per-fect - ly, And now our les-son's said.

PLAYTIME.

No. 3.

In march time.

1. March, march a-way! March, march a-way! To the play-ground lead the way: All our les-sons now are past,—

rather slower. *In time.*

Left foot first, and not too fast: On, 'tis nice, each sun-ny day, Thus to en-joy our-selves in play!

We'll no an-gry looks be-tray, But mer-ri-ly, mer-ri-ly march, march a-way! But mer-ri-ly, mer-ri-ly

-march, march a-way, march a-way, march a-way!....................

No. 4.

GRACE BEFORE MEALS.

Adagio non troppo.

1. Here, a lit - tle child, I stand, Heav - ing up my ei - ther hand; Cold as pad-docks

though they be, Here I lift them up to Thee, For a ben - i - son to fall On our meat and

on us all. A - men, A - - - men.......

No. 5.   A SONG OF A DOLL.

Con espressione.

1. I once had a sweet lit - tle doll, dears, The

pret - ti - est doll in the world;....... Her cheeks were so red and so white, dears, And her

hair was so charm - ing - ly curled :........ But I lost my poor lit - tle doll, dears, As I

played on the heath one day,....... And I cried for her more than a week, dears, But I

ne - ver could find where she lay, ... I ne - ver could find where she lay... ....

ad lib.

colla voce.

2. I

found my poor lit-tle doll, dears, As I played on the heath one day :........ Folks say she is ter-ri-bly

changed, dears, For her paint is all wash-ed a - way,...... And her arms trodden off by the cows, dears, And her

hair not the least bit curled :.... Yet for old sake's sake she is still, dears, The pret-ti-est doll in the

world,......... The pret-ti-est doll in the world......

No. 6.

A ROMP.

As fast as you will.

TIRED.

No. 7. *Grazioso.*

1. Oh, I'm so sleepy, I'll lie down to rest Here in the sun; Soon will he go to his bed in the west, Day will be done. Oh, I'm so slee - - py!

sleepily.

Soft is the grass, with the moss peep-ing through, Just like my bed;

By degrees, slower and more sleepily.   *p*   *dim.*   *pp*   *Adagio.*

Dai-sies are ga-zing up in-to the blue, O-ver my head. Oh, I'm so

Slower by degrees, with the voice.   *p*   *dim.*   *pp*   *pp*   *Adagio.*

Falls asleep

slee - - -

ppp

Both Pedals.

No. 8.
Andante non troppo.

CHILD'S PRAYER.

1. Je - sus, ten - der Shep - herd, hear me, Bless Thy lit - tle lamb to - night; Thro' the dark - ness
2. Let my sins be all for - giv - en, Bless the friends I love so well; Take me, when I

be Thou near me, Watch my sleep till morn - ing light: Je - sus, hear me! hear me, ten - der
die, to hea - ven, Hap - py there with Thee to dwell:

Shep - - herd!

No. 9.

SLEEPING.

1. Lul-la-by,   lul-la-by,   ba - by dear,   Take   thy rest with-out a   fear;
2. Lul-la-by,   lul-la-by,   gone is the light,   Yet let not darkness my ba - by fright,
3. *pp* May thy small dreams   no ill things see,   Kind heaven keep watch, my babe, o'er thee,

Qui - et   sleep,   for mo-ther is   here,.....   E - ver   wake - ful   e - ver near,
Mo - ther is   with her a - mid the   night ;...   Then soft - ly   sleep,   my heart's   de - light,
Kind an - gels   bright thy   guard - ians   be,.........   And give thee, smil-ing, to   day and to me,

E - - ver wake - ful,   e - ver near.   Lul - la - by,   lul - la - by!
Then soft - ly sleep, my   heart's de - light.   Lul - la - by   lul - la - by!
And give thee, smil - ing, to   day and to me.   Lul - la - by,   lul - la - by!

Endpaper from *A Day in a Child's Life*

The back cover of this book, shown here, was exactly like the front cover.

Selections

DEDICATED TO
GODFREY, DOROTHY, OLIVER & MAUD
CHILDREN OF FREDERICK LOCKER ESQ.

THE BOYS AND THE APPLE-TREE

As William and Thomas were walking one
    day,
    They came by a fine orchard's side:
They would rather eat apples than spell,
    read, or play,
    And Thomas to William then cried:

"O brother, look yonder! what clusters hang
    there!
    I'll try and climb over the wall:
I must have an apple; I will have a pear;
    Although it should cost me a fall!"

Said William to Thomas, "To steal is a sin,
    Mamma has oft told this to thee:
I never have stolen, nor will I begin,
    So the apples may hang on the tree."

"You are a good boy, as you ever have
    been,"
    Said Thomas, "let's walk on, my lad:
We'll call on our schoolfellow, Benjamin
    Green,
    Who to see us I know will be glad."

They came to the house, and ask'd at the
    gate,
    "Is Benjamin Green now at home?"
But Benjamin did not allow them to wait,
    And brought them both into the room.

And he smiled, and he laugh'd, and caper'd
    with joy,
    His little companions to greet:
"And we too are happy," said each little
    boy,
    "Our playfellow dear thus to meet."

"Come, walk in our garden, this morning
    so fine,
    We may, for my father gives leave;
And more, he invites you to stay here and
    dine:
    And a most happy day we shall have!"

But when in the garden, they found 'twas
    the same
    They saw as they walk'd in the road;
And near the high wall when those little
    boys came,
    They started as if from a toad:

"That large ring of iron, you see on the
    ground,
    With terrible teeth like a saw,"
Said their friend, "the guard of our garden
    is found,
    And it keeps all intruders in awe.

"If any the warning without set at naught,
    Their legs then this man-trap must tear:"
Said William to Thomas, "So you'd have
    been caught,
    If you had leapt over just there."

Cried Thomas in terror of what now he saw,
    "With my faults I will heartily grapple;
For I learn what may happen by breaking a law,
    Although but in stealing an apple."

THE ORPHAN.

My father and mother are dead,
　Nor friend, nor relation I know;
And now the cold earth is their bed,
　And daisies will over them grow.

I cast my eyes into the tomb,
　The sight made me bitterly cry;
I said, "And is this the dark room,
　Where my father and mother must lie?

I cast my eyes round me again,
　In hopes some protector to see;
Alas! but the search was in vain,
　For none had compassion on me.

I cast my eyes up to the sky,
　I groan'd, though I said not a word;
Yet God was not deaf to my cry,
　The friend of the fatherless heard.

For since I have trusted his care,
　And learn'd on his word to depend,
He has kept me from every snare,
　And been my best Father and Friend.

DIRTY JIM.

There was one little Jim,
'Tis reported of him,
   And must be to his lasting disgrace,
That he never was seen
With hands at all clean,
   Nor yet ever clean was his face.

His friends were much hurt
To see so much dirt,
   And often they made him quite clean;
But all was in vain,
He got dirty again,
   And not at all fit to be seen.

It gave him no pain
To hear them complain,
   Nor his own dirty clothes to survey:
His indolent mind
No pleasure could find
   In tidy and wholesome array.

The idle and bad,
Like this little lad,
   May love dirty ways, to be sure;
But good boys are seen
To be decent and clean,
   Although they are ever so poor.

MEDDLESOME MATTY.

One ugly trick has often spoil'd
  The sweetest and the best;
Matilda, though a pleasant child,
  One ugly trick possess'd,
Which like a cloud before the skies,
Hid all her better qualities.

Sometimes she'd lift the tea-pot lid,
  To peep at what was in it;
Or tilt the kettle, if you did
  But turn your back a minute.
In vain you told her not to touch,
Her trick of meddling grew so much.

Her grandmamma went out one day,
  And by mistake she laid
Her spectacles and snuff-box gay
  Too near the little maid;
"Ah! well," thought she, "I'll try them on,
As soon as grandmamma is gone."

Forthwith she placed upon her nose
  The glasses large and wide;
And looking round, as I suppose,
  The snuff-box too she spied:
"Oh! what a pretty box is that;
I'll open it," said little Matt.

"I know that grandmamma would say,
  'Don't meddle with it, dear;'
But then, she's far enough away,
  And no one else is near:
Besides, what can there be amiss
In opening such a box as this?"

So thumb and finger went to work
To move the stubborn lid,
And presently a mighty jerk
  The mighty mischief did;
For all at once, ah! woful case,
The snuff came puffing in her face.

Poor eyes, and nose, and mouth, beside
  A dismal sight presented;
In vain, as bitterly she cried,
  Her folly she repented.
In vain she ran about for ease;
She could do nothing now but sneeze.

She dash'd the spectacles away,
  To wipe her tingling eyes,
And as in twenty bits they lay,
  Her grandmamma she spies.
"Heyday! and what's the matter now?"
Says grandmamma, with lifted brow.

Matilda, smarting with the pain,
  And tingling still, and sore,
Made many a promise to refrain
  From meddling evermore.
And 'tis a fact, as I have heard,
She ever since has kept her word.

THE GAUDY FLOWER.

Why does my Anna toss her head,
　And look so scornfully around,
As if she scarcely deign'd to tread
　Upon the daisy-dappled ground?

Does fancied beauty fire thine eye,
　The brilliant tint, the satin skin?
Does the loved glass, in passing by,
　Reflect a graceful form and thin?

Alas! that form, and brilliant fire,
　Will never win beholder's love
It may, indeed, make fools admire,
　But ne'er the wise and good can move.

So grows the tulip, gay and bold,
　The broadest sunshine its delight;
Like rubies, or like burnish'd gold,
　It shows its petals, glossy bright.

But who the gaudy flowered crops,
　As if to court a sweet perfume!
Admired it blows, neglected drops,
　And sinks unheeded to its doom.

The virtues of the heart may move
　Affections of a genial kind;
While beauty fails to stir our love,
　And wins the eye, but not the mind.

SLEEPY HARRY.

"I do not like to go to bed,"
Sleepy little Harry said;
"Go, naughty Betty, go away,
I will not come at all, I say!"

Oh, silly child! what is he saying!
As if he could be always playing!
Then, Betty, you must come and carry
This very foolish little Harry.

The little birds are better taught,
They go to roosting when they ought;
And all the ducks, and fowls, you know,
They went to bed an hour ago.

The little beggar in the street,
Who wanders with his naked feet,
And has not where to lay his head,
Oh, he'd be glad to go to bed.

COME AND PLAY IN THE GARDEN.

Little sister, come away,
And let us in the garden play,
For it is a pleasant day.

On the grass-plat let us sit,
Or, if you please, we'll play a bit,
And run about all over it.

But the fruit we will not pick,
For what would be a naughty trick,
And very likely make us sick.

Nor will we pluck the pretty flowers
That grow about the beds and bowers,
Because you know they are not ours.

We'll take the daisies, white and red,
Because mamma has often said
That we may gather them instead.

And much I hope we always may
Our very dear mamma obey,
And mind whatever she may say.

THE VILLAGE GREEN.

On the cheerful village green,
  Skirted round with houses small,
All the boys and girls are seen,
  Playing there with hoop and ball.

Now they frolic hand in hand,
  Making many a merry chain;
Then they form a warlike band,
  Marching o'er the level plain.

Now ascends the worsted ball,
  High it rises in the air,
Or against the cottage wall,
  Up and down it bounces there.

Then the hoop, with even pace,
  Runs before the merry throngs;
Joy is seen in every face,
  Joy is heard in cheerful songs.

Rich array, and mansions proud,
  Gilded toys, and costly fare,
Would not make the little crowd
  Half so happy as they are.

Then, contented with my state,
  Where true pleasure may be seen,
Let me envy not the great,
  On a cheerful village green.

KATE GREENAWAY'S
PAINTING BOOK

LONDON
FREDERICK WARNE & Co Ltd
& NEW YORK.

THE Examples of the delightful Drawings of Miss Kate Greenaway given in the following pages have been selected from her well-known Children's Books and Calendars. Included in the former are, " Under the Window " and "A Day in a Child's Life."

Young eyes are keen to recognise beauty. Thus, in giving a selection of the work of some of our great artists in the form of a Series of Painting Books, of which this Volume is one; the aim has been to place the child on a simple road of appreciation of all that is best in Art. The earlier the intro-duction, the sooner will a desire mani-fest itself for those forms of Art that help so much to beautify our lives.

*   *   *

Simple practical Directions for Colouring are given at the end of this book.

Selections

175

A Few Practical Directions for Colouring.

A GOOD PAINT BOX may be obtained from any Artist's Colourman or Stationer, and should contain the following colours :—

IVORY BLACK.	CRIMSON LAKE.	GAMBOGE.
SEPIA.	VERMILION.	EMERALD GREEN.
VANDYKE BROWN.	LIGHT RED.	PRUSSIAN BLUE.
BURNT SIENNA.	YELLOW OCHRE.	ULTRAMARINE.

THE BRUSHES must be washed clean, rinsed, and dried after use. Never leave the Brushes in the water, and never lay them flat on the table. Take plenty of colour in your Brush. Try first on a piece of spare paper to see that you have the right shade, and that your Brush is not too wet or too dry.

Always begin at the top and colour *downwards*, from your left to your right hand.

The edge of a colour may be softened with a clean damp Brush.

RED, BLUE, and YELLOW are *simple* colours, and cannot be made by mixing.

ORANGE, PURPLE, and GREEN are *compound* colours, and are made by mixing *simple* colours as follows :—

For PURPLE *mix* RED and BLUE.

For GREEN *mix* YELLOW and BLUE.

For ORANGE *mix* RED and YELLOW.

For GREY *mix* PRUSSIAN BLUE, LAKE, and SEPIA.

ULTRAMARINE is the purest BLUE, but it does not mix so well as the PRUSSIAN BLUE. It is useful for skies and for the grey shades in flowers.

All cold colours which are to serve as shadows to warmer colours should be laid on first, and generally warm colours over cold should be the rule. BLUE is a very cold colour, LAKE is a colder RED than VERMILION or LIGHT RED, and GAMBOGE is a colder YELLOW than OCHRE.

ORANGE is the warmest colour in nature, and BLUE is the coldest. RED and YELLOW are warm in proportion as they approach the ORANGE tint.

Kate Greenaway's
Picture Books.

UNDER THE WINDOW.
Pictures & Rhymes.

MARIGOLD GARDEN.
Pictures & Rhymes.

THE PIED PIPER OF HAMELIN.
By Robert Browning.
Illustrated by Kate Greenaway.

LITTLE ANN & OTHER POEMS.
By Jane & Ann Taylor.
Illustrated by Kate Greenaway.

MOTHER GOOSE,
or, the old Nursery Rhymes.

KATE GREENAWAY'S
BIRTHDAY BOOK.

THE MARIGOLD
PAINTING BOOK.

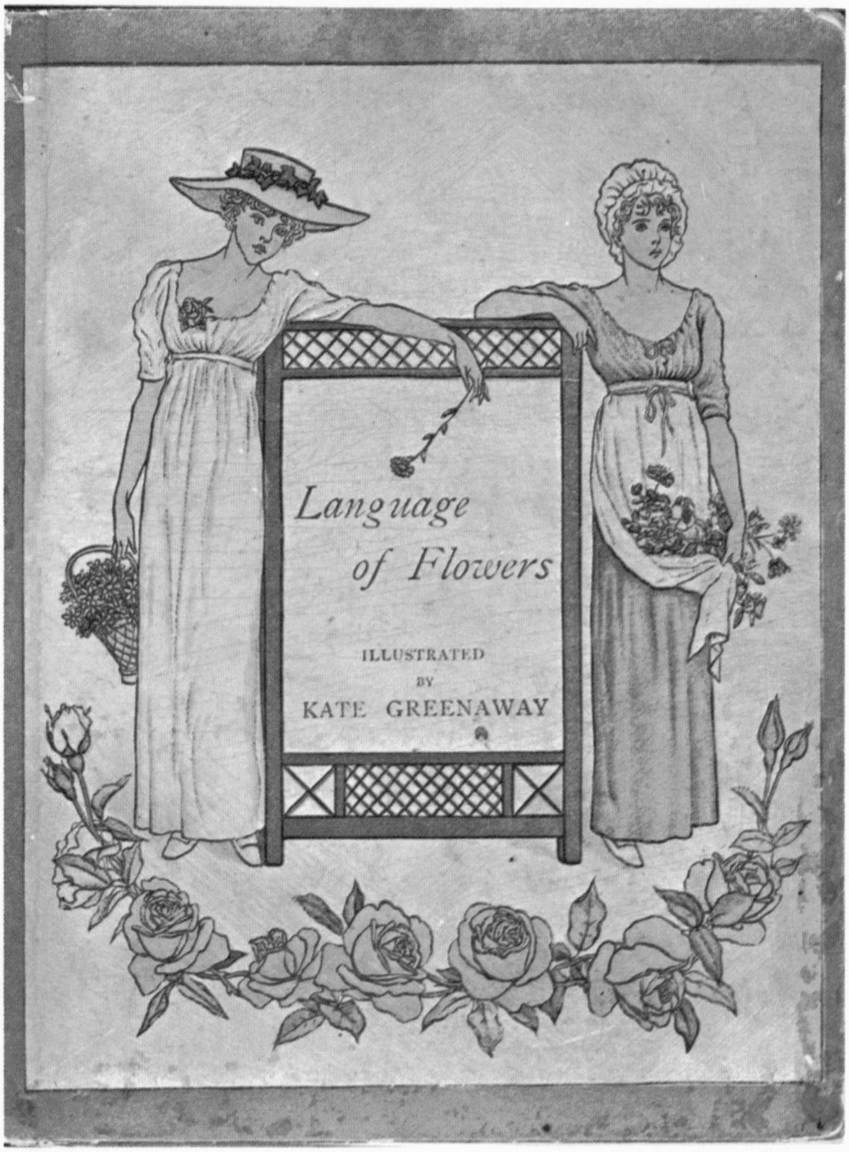

Partial text and illustrations

LANGUAGE·OF·FLOWERS

Language of Flowers

ILLUSTRATED BY

KATE GREENAWAY

PRINTED IN COLOURS BY

EDMUND EVANS

—:o:—

Abecedary	. . . .	*Volubility.*
Abatina	. . . .	*Fickleness.*
Acacia	. . . .	*Friendship.*
Acacia, Rose or White	.	*Elegance.*
Acacia, Yellow	. .	*Secret love.*
Acanthus	. . .	*The fine arts.* *Artifice.*
Acalia	. . .	*Temperance.*
Achillea Millefolia	.	*War.*
Aconite (Wolfsbane)	.	*Misanthropy.*
Aconite, Crowfoot	. .	*Lustre.*
Adonis, Flos	. . .	*Painful recollections.*
African Marigold	. .	*Vulgar minds.*
Agnus Castus	. .	*Coldness. Indifference.*
Agrimony	. . .	*Thankfulness. Gratitude.*
Almond (Common).	.	*Stupidity. Indiscretion.*

Bachelor's Buttons .	. .	*Celibacy.*
Balm	. . . .	*Sympathy.*
Balm, Gentle .	. .	*Pleasantry.*
Balm of Gilead	. .	*Cure. Relief.*
Balsam, Red .	, . .	*Touch me not. Impatient resolves.*
Balsam, Yellow	. .	*Impatience.*
Barberry	. . .	*Sourness of temper*
Barberry Tree	. .	*Sharpness.*
Basil	. . . .	*Hatred.*
Bay Leaf	. . .	*I change but in death.*
Bay (Rose) Rhododendron	.	*Danger. Beware.*
Bay Tree	. . .	*Glory.*
Bay Wreath	. . .	*Reward of merit.*
Bearded Crepis	. .	*Protection.*
Beech Tree	. . .	*Prosperity.*
Bee Orchis	. . .	*Industry.*
Bee Ophrys	. . .	*Error.*
Belladonna	. . .	*Silence.*
Bell Flower, Pyramidal .		*Constancy.*
Bell Flower (small white)		*Gratitude.*

Cabbage	. *Profit.*
Cacalia	. *Adulation.*
Cactus	. *Warmth.*
Calla Æthiopica . .	. *Magnificent Beauty.*
Calycanthus . . .	. *Benevolence.*
Camellia Japonica, Red	. *Unpretending excellence.*
Camellia Japonica, White	. *Perfected loveliness.*
Camomile . . .	. *Energy in adversity.*
Canary Grass . . .	. *Perseverance.*
Candytuft . . .	. *Indifference.*
Canterbury Bell . .	. *Acknowledgement.*
Cape Jasmine . .	. *I'm too happy.*
Cardamine . . .	. *Paternal error.*
Carnation, Deep Red .	. *Alas! for my poor heart.*
Carnation, Striped . .	. *Refusal.*
Carnation, Yellow . .	. *Disdain.*

Daffodil	. *Regard.*
Dahlia	. *Instability.*
Daisy . . .	. *Innocence.*
Daisy, Garden . .	. *I share your sentiments*
Daisy, Michaelmas .	. *Farewell.*
Daisy, Party-coloured .	. *Beauty.*
Daisy, Wild . .	. *I will think of it.*
Damask Rose . .	. *Brilliant complexion.*
Dandelion . .	. *Rustic oracle.*
Daphne Odora . .	. *Painting the lily.*
Darnel (Ray grass). .	. *Vice*
Dead Leaves . . .	. *Sadness.*
Dew Plant . . .	. *A Serenade.*
Dittany of Crete . .	. *Birth.*
Dittany of Crete, White	. *Passion.*
Dock	. *Patience.*
Dodder of Thyme . .	. *Baseness.*
Dogsbane . . .	. *Deceit. Falsehood.*
Dogwood . . .	. *Durability.*
Dragon Plant . .	. *Snare.*
Dragonwort . . .	. *Horror.*
Dried Flax . . .	. *Utility.*

Ebony Tree . . .	. *Blackness.*
Eglantine (Sweetbrier) .	. *Poetry. I wound to heal.*
Elder	. *Zealousness.*
Elm	. *Dignity.*
Enchanter's Nightshade	. *Witchcraft. Sorcery.*
Endive . . .	. *Frugality.*
Eupatorium . . .	. *Delay.*
Everflowering Candytuft	. *Indifference.*
Evergreen Clematis .	. *Poverty.*
Evergreen Thorn . .	. *Solace in adversity.*
Everlasting . . .	. *Never-ceasing remembrance.*
Everlasting Pea . .	. *Lasting pleasure.*

Fennel	. *Worthy all praise. Strength.*
Fern . . .	. *Fascination.*
Ficoides, Ice Plant .	. *Your looks freeze me.*
Fig	. *Argument.*
Fig Marigold . . .	. *Idleness.*
Fig Tree . . .	. *Prolific.*
Filbert . . .	. *Reconciliation*
Fir	. *Time.*
Fir Tree . . .	. *Elevation.*
Flax . . .	. *Domestic Industry. Fate.*
	I feel your kindness.
Flax-leaved Goldy-locks	. *Tardiness.*
Fleur-de-Lis . . .	. *Flame. I burn.*
Fleur-de-Luce . .	. *Fire.*
Flowering Fern . .	. *Reverie.*
Flowering Reed .	. *Confidence in Heaven.*
Flower-of-an-Hour .	. *Delicate beauty.*
Fly Orchis . . .	. *Error.*

Flytrap	.	*Deceit.*
Fool's Parsley . .	.	*Silliness.*
Forget Me Not . .	.	*True love. Forget me not.*
Foxglove . . .	.	*Insincerity.*
Foxtail Grass . . .	.	*Sporting.*
French Honeysuckle .	.	*Rustic beauty.*
French Marigold . .	.	*Jealousy.*
French Willow . .	.	*Bravery and humanity.*
Frog Ophrys . .	.	*Disgust.*
Fuller's Teasel . .	.	*Misanthropy.*
Fumitory . . .	.	*Spleen.*
Fuchsia, Scarlet . .	.	*Taste.*

Garden Anemone . .	.	*Forsaken.*
Garden Chervil . .	.	*Sincerity.*
Garden Daisy . .	.	*I partake your sentiments.*
Garden Marigold . .	.	*Uneasiness.*
Garden Ranunculus .	.	*You are rich in attractions.*
Garden Sage . . .	.	*Esteem.*
Garland of Roses . .	.	*Reward of virtue.*
Germander Speedwell .	.	*Facility.*
Geranium, Dark . .	.	*Melancholy.*
Geranium, Ivy . .	.	*Bridal favour.*
Geranium, Lemon . .	.	*Unexpected meeting.*
Geranium, Nutmeg .	.	*Expected meeting.*
Geranium, Oak-leaved .	.	*True friendship.*
Geranium, Pencilled .	.	*Ingenuity.*
Geranium, Rose-scented .	.	*Preference.*
Geranium, Scarlet . .	.	*Comforting. Stupidity.*
Geranium, Silver-leaved .	.	*Recall.*
Geranium, Wild .	.	*Steadfast piety.*

Hand Flower Tree . . .	*Warning.*
Harebell	*Submission. Grief.*
Hawkweed . . .	*Quicksightedness.*
Hawthorn . . .	*Hope.*
Hazel	*Reconciliation.*
Heath	*Solitude.*
Helenium . . .	*Tears.*
Heliotrope . . .	*Devotion. Faithfulness.*
Hellebore . . .	*Scandal. Calumny.*
Helmet Flower (Monkshood).	*Knight-errantry.*
Hemlock . . .	*You will be my death.*
Hemp	*Fate.*
Henbane . . .	*Imperfection.*
Hepatica . . .	*Confidence.*
Hibiscus . . .	*Delicate beauty.*
Holly	*Foresight.*
Holly Herb . . .	*Enchantment.*
Hollyhock . . .	*Ambition. Fecundity.*
Honesty	*Honesty. Fascination.*

Iceland Moss . . .	*Health.*
Ice Plant . . .	*Your looks freeze me*
Imperial Montague .	*Power.*
Indian Cress . . .	*Warlike trophy.*
Indian Jasmine (Ipomœa) .	*Attachment.*
Indian Pink (Double) .	*Always lovely.*
Indian Plum . .	*Privation.*
Iris	*Message.*
Iris, German . . .	*Flame.*
Ivy	*Fidelity. Marriage.*
Ivy, Sprig of, with tendrils	*Assiduous to please.*

Jacob's Ladder	.	.	. *Come down.*
Japan Rose	.	.	. *Beauty is your only attraction.*
Jasmine	.	.	. *Amiability.*
Jasmine, Cape	.	.	. *Transport of joy.*
Jasmine, Carolina	.	.	. *Separation.*
Jasmine, Indian	.	.	. *I attach myself to you.*
Jasmine, Spanish	.	.	. *Sensuality.*
Jasmine, Yellow	.	.	. *Grace and elegance.*
Jonquil	.	.	. *I desire a return of affection.*
Judas Tree	.	.	. *Unbelief. Betrayal.*
Juniper	.	.	. *Succour. Protection.*
Justicia	.	.	. *The perfection of female loveliness.*

Kennedia	.	.	. *Mental Beauty.*
King-cups	.	.	. *Desire of Riches.*

Laburnum	. . .	*Forsaken. Pensive Beauty.*
Lady's Slipper	. . .	*Capricious Beauty. Win me and wear me.*
Lagerstræmia, Indian	.	*Eloquence.*
Lantana	. . .	*Rigour.*
Larch	. . .	*Audacity. Boldness.*
Larkspur	. . .	*Lightness. Levity.*
Larkspur, Pink	. .	*Fickleness.*
Larkspur, Purple	. .	*Haughtiness.*
Laurel	. . .	*Glory.*
Laurel, Common, in flower	.	*Perfidy.*
Laurel, Ground	. .	*Perseverance.*
Laurel, Mountain	. .	*Ambition.*
Laurel-leaved Magnolia	.	*Dignity.*
Laurestina	. .	*A token. I die if neglected.*
Lavender	. . .	*Distrust.*
Leaves (dead)	. .	*Melancholy.*
Lemon	. . .	*Zest.*
Lemon Blossoms	. .	*Fidelity in love.*
Lettuce	. . .	*Cold-heartedness.*
Lichen	. . .	*Dejection. Solitude.*

Lilac, Field	. . .	*Humility.*
Lilac, Purple	. .	*First emotions of love.*
Lilac, White	. .	*Youthful Innocence.*
Lily, Day	. .	*Coquetry.*
Lily, Imperial	. .	*Majesty.*
Lily, White	. .	*Purity. Sweetness.*
Lily, Yellow	. .	*Falsehood. Gaiety.*
Lily of the Valley	.	*Return of happiness.*
Linden or Lime Trees	.	*Conjugal love.*
Lint	. . .	*I feel my obligations.*
Live Oak	. .	*Liberty.*
Liverwort	. .	*Confidence.*
Licorice, Wild	. .	*I declare against you.*
Lobelia	. . .	*Malevolence.*
Locust Tree	. .	*Elegance.*
Locust Tree (green)	.	*Affection beyond the grave.*
London Pride	. .	*Frivolity.*
Lote Tree	. .	*Concord.*
Lotus	. . .	*Eloquence.*
Lotus Flower	. .	*Estranged love.*
Lotus Leaf	. .	*Recantation.*
Love in a Mist	. .	*Perplexity.*
Love lies Bleeding	.	*Hopeless, not heartless.*
Lucern	. . .	*Life.*
Lupine	. . .	*Voraciousness. Imagination.*

Madder	*Calumny.*
Magnolia . . .	*Love of Nature.*
Magnolia, Swamp . .	*Perseverance.*
Mallow	*Mildness.*
Mallow, Marsh . .	*Beneficence.*
Mallow, Syrian . .	*Consumed by love.*
Mallow, Venetian . .	*Delicate beauty.*
Manchineal Tree . .	*Falsehood.*
Mandrake . . .	*Horror.*
Maple	*Reserve.*
Marigold. . . .	*Grief.*
Marigold, African .	*Vulgar minds.*
Marigold, French . .	*Jealousy.*
Marigold, Prophetic .	*Prediction.*
Marigold and Cypress .	*Despair.*
Marjoram . . .	*Blushes.*
Marvel of Peru . .	*Timidity.*

Narcissus . . .	*Egotism.*
Nasturtium . . .	*Patriotism.*
Nettle, Burning . .	*Slander.*
Nettle Tree . .	*Concert.*
Night-blooming Cereus .	*Transient beauty.*
Night Convolvulus .	*Night.*
Nightshade . .	*Truth.*

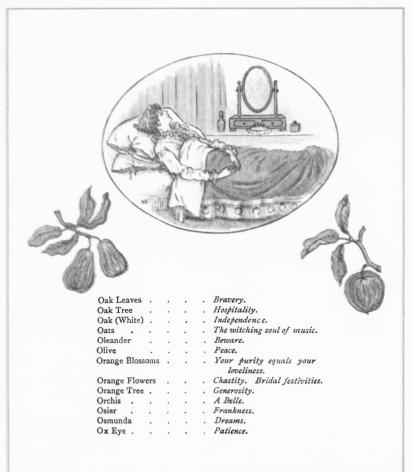

Oak Leaves	. . .	.	*Bravery.*
Oak Tree	. . .	.	*Hospitality.*
Oak (White)	. . .	.	*Independence.*
Oats	. . .	.	*The witching soul of music.*
Oleander	. . .	.	*Beware.*
Olive	. . .	.	*Peace.*
Orange Blossoms	. .	.	*Your purity equals your loveliness.*
Orange Flowers	. .	.	*Chastity. Bridal festivities.*
Orange Tree	. . .	.	*Generosity.*
Orchis	. . .	.	*A Belle.*
Osier	. . .	.	*Frankness.*
Osmunda	. . .	.	*Dreams.*
Ox Eye	. . .	.	*Patience.*

Palm	. . .	.	*Victory.*
Pansy	. . .	.	*Thoughts.*
Parsley	. . .	.	*Festivity.*
Pasque Flower	. .	.	*You have no claims.*
Passion Flower	. .	.	*Religious superstition.*
Patience Dock	. .	.	*Patience.*
Pea, Everlasting	. .	.	*An appointed meeting. Lasting Pleasure.*
Pea, Sweet	. . .	.	*Departure.*
Peach	. . .	.	*Your qualities, like your charms, are unequalled.*
Peach Blossom	. .	.	*I am your captive.*
Pear	. . .	.	*Affection.*
Pear Tree	. . .	.	*Comfort.*
Pennyroyal	. . .	.	*Flee away.*
Peony	. . .	.	*Shame. Bashfulness.*
Peppermint	. . .	.	*Warmth of feeling.*
Periwinkle, Blue	. .	.	*Early friendship.*
Periwinkle, White	. .	.	*Pleasures of memory.*
Persicaria	. . .	.	*Restoration.*

Quaking-Grass	.		Agitation.
Quamoclit	.		Busybody.
Queen's Rocket	. . .	You are the queen of coquettes. Fashion.
Quince	. . . .	Temptation.

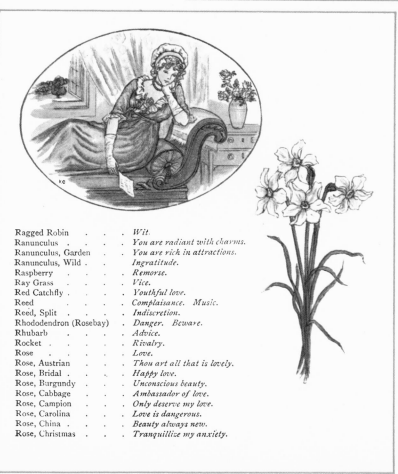

Ragged Robin	. .	Wit.
Ranunculus	. . .	You are radiant with charms.
Ranunculus, Garden	.	You are rich in attractions.
Ranunculus, Wild	.	Ingratitude.
Raspberry	. . .	Remorse.
Ray Grass	. .	Vice.
Red Catchfly	. .	Youthful love.
Reed	. . .	Complaisance. Music.
Reed, Split	. . .	Indiscretion.
Rhododendron (Rosebay)	.	Danger. Beware.
Rhubarb	. . .	Advice.
Rocket	. . .	Rivalry.
Rose	. . .	Love.
Rose, Austrian	. .	Thou art all that is lovely.
Rose, Bridal	. .	Happy love.
Rose, Burgundy	. .	Unconscious beauty.
Rose, Cabbage	. .	Ambassador of love.
Rose, Campion	. .	Only deserve my love.
Rose, Carolina	. .	Love is dangerous.
Rose, China	. .	Beauty always new.
Rose, Christmas	. .	Tranquillize my anxiety.

Saffron	*Beware of excess.*
Saffron Crocus . .	*Mirth.*
Saffron, Meadow . .	*My happiest days are past.*
Sage	*Domestic virtue.*
Sage, Garden . .	*Esteem.*
Sainfoin . . .	*Agitation.*
Saint John's Wort . .	*Animosity. Superstition.*
Sardony . . .	*Irony.*
Saxifrage, Mossy . .	*Affection.*
Scabious . . .	*Unfortunate love.*
Scabious, Sweet . .	*Widowhood.*
Scarlet Lychnis . .	*Sunbeaming eyes.*
Schinus . . .	*Religious enthusiasm.*
Scotch Fir . .	*Elevation.*
Sensitive Plant . .	*Sensibility. Delicate feelings.*
Senvy . . .	*Indifference.*
Shamrock . . .	*Light heartedness.*
Snakesfoot . . .	*Horror.*

Tamarisk	*Crime.*
Tansy (Wild). . .	*I declare war against you*
Teasel	*Misanthropy.*
Tendrils of Climbing Plants	*Ties.*
Thistle, Common .	*Austerity.*
Thistle, Fuller's . .	*Misanthropy*
Thistle, Scotch . .	*Retaliation.*
Thorn Apple . .	*Deceitful charms.*
Thorn, Branch of .	*Severity.*
Thrift . . .	*Sympathy.*
Throatwort . .	*Neglected beauty.*
Thyme. . . .	*Activity.*
Tiger Flower . .	*For once may pride befriend me.*
Traveller's Joy . .	*Safety.*
Tree of Life . .	*Old age.*
Trefoil	*Revenge.*

Tremella Nestoc	.	.	.	Resistance.
Trillium Pictum	.	.	.	Modest beauty.
Truffle	.	.	.	Surprise.
Trumpet Flower	.	.	.	Fame.
Tuberose	.	.	.	Dangerous pleasures.
Tulip	.	.	.	Fame.
Tulip, Red	.	.	.	Declaration of love.
Tulip, Variegated	.	.	.	Beautiful eyes.
Tulip, Yellow	.	.	.	Hopeless love.
Turnip	.	.	.	Charity.
Tussilage (Sweet-scented)	.	.	Justice shall be done you.

Valerian	.	.	.	An accommodating disposition.
Valerian, Greek	.	.	Rupture.
Venice Sumach	.	.	Intellectual excellence Splendour.
Venus' Car	.	.	Fly with me.
Venus' Looking-glass	.	Flattery.
Venus' Trap	.	.	Deceit.
Vernal Grass	.	.	Poor, but happy.
Veronica	.	.	.	Fidelity.
Vervain	.	.	.	Enchantment.
Vine	.	.	.	Intoxication.
Violet, Blue	.	.	Faithfulness.
Violet, Dame	.	.	Watchfulness.
Violet, Sweet	.	.	Modesty.
Violet, Yellow	.	.	Rural happiness.
Virginian Spiderwort	.	Momentary happiness.
Virgin's Bower	.	.	Filial love.
Volkamenia	.	.	May you be happy.

Walnut	.	.	.	Intellect. Stratagem.
Wall-flower	.	.	.	Fidelity in adversity.
Water Lily	.	.	.	Purity of heart.
Water Melon	.	.	Bulkiness.
Wax Plant	.	.	Susceptibility.
Wheat Stalk	.	.	Riches.
Whin	.	.	.	Anger.
White Jasmine	.	.	Amiableness.
White Lily	.	.	Purity and Modesty.
White Mullein	.	.	Good nature.
White Oak	.	.	Independence.
White Pink	.	.	Talent.
White Poplar	.	.	Time.
White Rose (dried)	.	.	Death preferable to loss of innocence.
Whortleberry	.	.	Treason.
Willow, Creeping	.	.	Love forsaken.
Willow, Water	.	.	Freedom.

| Xanthium | . | . | . | . | Ruaeness. Pertinacity. |
| Xeranthemum | . | . | . | Cheerfulness under adversity. |

Yew . . . . . *Sorrow*

Zephyr Flower . . . *Expectation.*
Zinnia . . . . . *Thoughts of absent friends*

MARIGOLD GARDEN

By
Kate Greenaway

MARIGOLD GARDEN

BY KATE GREENAWAY

Partial text and illustrations

MARIGOLD GARDEN

·

Pictures and Rhymes

by

KATE GREENAWAY

SUSAN BLUE.

OH, Susan Blue,
How do you do?
Please may I go for a walk with you?
Where shall we go?
Oh, I know—
Down in the meadow where the cowslips grow!

WISHES.

OH, if you were a little boy,
    And I was a little girl—
Why you would have some whiskers grow
    And then my hair would curl.

Ah! if I could have whiskers grow,
    I'd let you have my curls;
But what's the use of wishing it—
    Boys never can be girls.

WHEN WE WENT OUT WITH GRANDMAMMA.

WHEN we went out with Grandmamma—
   Mamma said for a treat—
Oh, dear, how stiff we had to walk
   As we went down the street.

One on each side we had to go,
   And never laugh or loll;
I carried Prim, her Spaniard dog
   And Tom—her parasol.

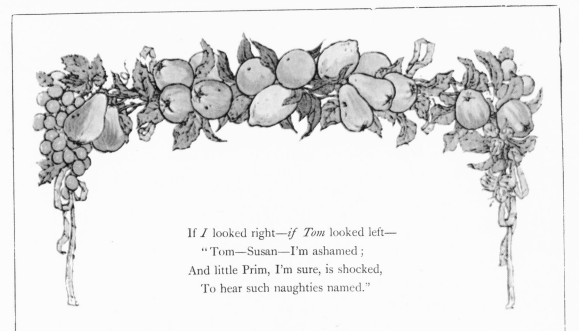

If *I* looked right—*if Tom* looked left—
  "Tom—Susan—I'm ashamed;
And little Prim, I'm sure, is shocked,
  To hear such naughties named."

She said we had no manners,
  If we ever talked or sung;
"You should have seen," said Grandmamma,
  "*Me* walk, when *I* was young."

She said they never wished then
  To play—oh, no, indeed!
They learnt to sew and needlework,
  Or else to write and read.

She told us—oh, so often—
  How little girls and boys,
In the good days when she was young,
  Never made any noise.

She said her mother never let
  Her speak a word at meals;
"But now," said Grandmamma, "you'd think
  That children's tongues had wheels

"So fast they go—clack, clack, clack, clack;
  Now listen well, I pray,
And let me see you both improve
  From what I've said to-day."

TO MYSTERY LAND.

Oh, dear, how will it end?
Peggy and Susie how naughty
    you are.
You little know where you are,
Going so far, and so high,
Nearly up to the sky.
Perhaps it's a Giant who
    lives there,
And perhaps it's a lovely
    Princess.
But you very well know
You've no business to go;
You'll get yourselves into a mess.

Oh, dear, I'm sure it is true;
Whatever on earth can it matter
    to you?
For you know it—oh, fie—
That it's naughty to pry
Into other's affairs—
Into other folks houses to go,
Where you know
You're not asked.
So you'd better come back
While there's time, it is plain.
Go home—and be never
So naughty again.

WHEN YOU AND I GROW UP.

When you and I
Grow up—Polly—
   I mean that you and me,
Shall go sailing in a big ship
   Right over all the sea.
We'll wait till we are older,
   For if we went to day,
You know that we might lose ourselves,
   And never find the way.

THE WEDDING BELLS.

THE Wedding Bells were ringing,
  And Monday was the day,
And all the little ladies
  Were there so fresh and gay.

And up—up—up the steps they went,
  The wedding fine to see ;
And the Roses were all for the Bride,
  So pretty—so pretty was she.

TO BABY.

OH, what shall my blue eyes go see?
  Shall it be pretty Quack-Quack to-day?
Or the Peacock upon the Yew Tree?
  Or the dear little white Lambs at play?
    Say Baby.
For Baby is such a young Petsy,
  And Baby is such a sweet Dear.
And Baby is growing quite old now—
  She's just getting on for a year.

AT SCHOOL.

FIVE little Girls, sitting on a form,
Five little Girls, with lessons to learn ;
Five little Girls, who, I'm afraid,
Won't know them a bit when they have to be said.

For little eyes are given to look
Anywhere else than on their book ;
And little thoughts are given to stray
Anywhere—ever so far away.

UNDER ROSE ARCHES.

UNDER Rose Arches to Rose Town—
　Rose Town on the top of the hill;
For the Summer wind blows and music goes,
　And the violins sound shrill.

Oh, Roses shall be for her carpet,
　And her curtains of Roses so fair;
And a Rosy crown, while far adown
　Floats her long golden hair.

Twist and twine Roses and Lilies,
　And little leaves green,
　Fit for a queen;
Twist and twine Roses and Lilies.

Twist and twine Roses and Lilies,
　And all the bells ring,
　And the people sing;
Twist and twine Roses and Lilies.

BABY MINE.

BABY mine, over the trees ·
    Baby mine, over the flowers ;
Baby mine, over the sunshine ;
    Baby mine, over the showers.

Baby mine, over the land ;
    Baby mine, over the water.
Oh, when had a mother before
    Such a sweet—such a sweet, little daughter !

ON THE BRIDGE.

IF I could see a little fish—
That is what I just now wish!
I want to see his great round eyes
Always open in surprise.

I wish a water-rat would glide
Slowly to the other side ;
Or a dancing spider sit
On the yellow flags a bit.

I think I'll get some stones to throw
And watch the pretty circles show.
Or shall we sail a flower-boat,
And watch it slowly—slowly float ?

That's nice—because you never know
How far away it means to go ;
And when to-morrow comes, you see,
It may be in the great wide sea.

THE CATS HAVE COME TO TEA.

WHAT did she see—oh, what did she see,
As she stood leaning against the tree?
Why all the Cats had come to tea.

What a fine turn out—from round about,
All the houses had let them out,
And here they were with scamper and shout.

"Mew—mew—mew!" was all they could say,
And, "We hope we find you well to-day."

Oh, what should she do—oh, what should she do?
What a lot of milk they would get through;
For here they were with "Mew—mew—mew!"

She didn't know—oh, she didn't know,
If bread and butter they'd like or no;
They might want little mice, oh! oh! oh!

Dear me—oh, dear me,
All the cats had come to tea.

THE LITTLE JUMPING GIRLS.

Jump—jump—jump—
    Jump away
From this town into
    The next, to-day.

Jump—jump—jump—
    Jump over the moon;
Jump all the morning,
    And all the noon.

Jump—jump—jump—
   Jump all night;
Won't our mothers
   Be in a fright?

Jump—jump—jump—
   Over the sea;
What wonderful wonders
   We shall see.

Jump—jump—jump—
   And leave behind
Everything evil
   That we may find.

Jump—jump—jump—
   Jump far away;
And all come home
   Some other day.

Complete text and illustrations

A a

B b

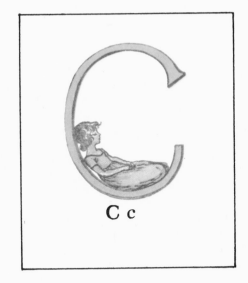

C c

D d

E e

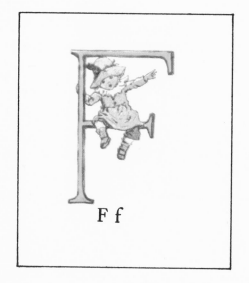

F f

G g

H h

I i

J j

K k

L l

M m

N n

O o

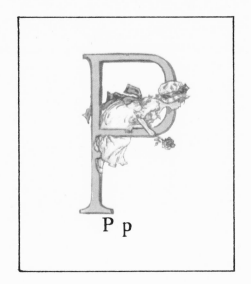

P p

Q q

R r

S s

T t

U u

V v

W w

X x

Y y

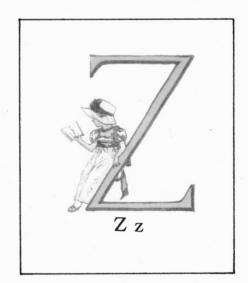

Z z

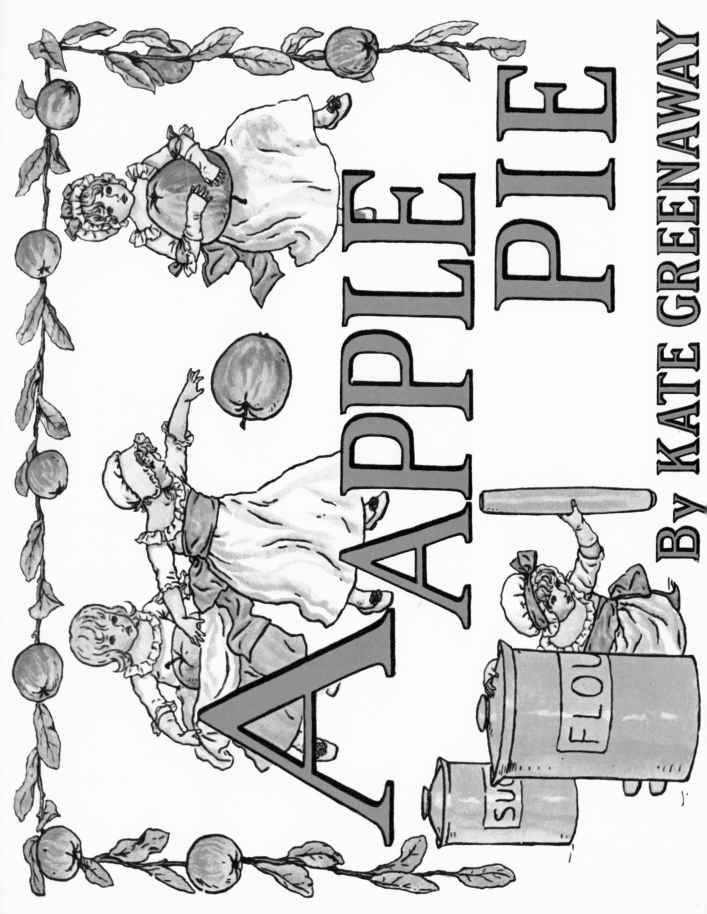

A APPLE PIE

By KATE GREENAWAY

A APPLE PIE

Complete text and illustrations

B BIT IT

CUT IT

DEALT IT

E

EAT IT

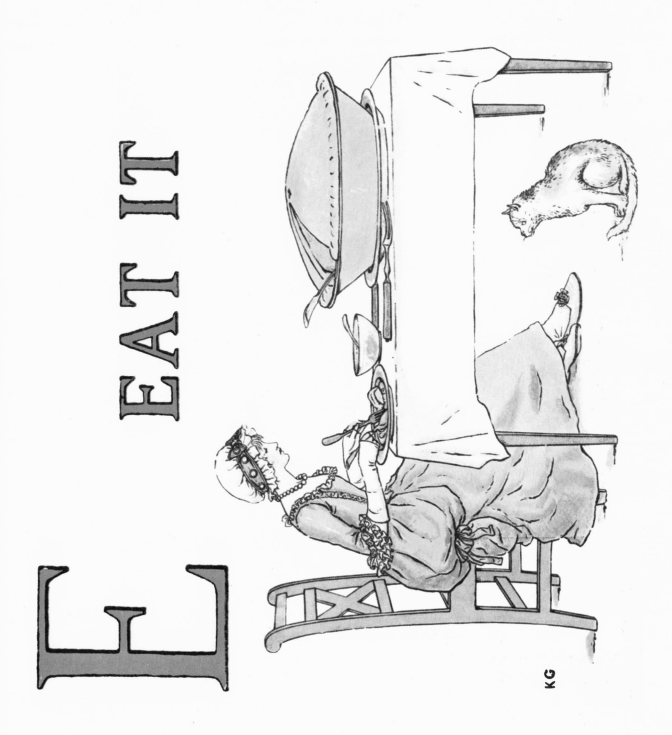

KG

F FOUGHT FOR IT

GOT IT

H

HAD IT

J JUMPED FOR IT

Editor's note: The text for this book was taken by Kate Greenaway from a very old rhyme written before the English alphabet contained the letter "I." Miss Greenaway omitted this letter purposely, following the traditional version.

KC

237

K KNELT FOR IT

L LONGED FOR IT

M MOURNED FOR IT

N NODDED FOR IT

OPENED IT

P PEEPED IN IT

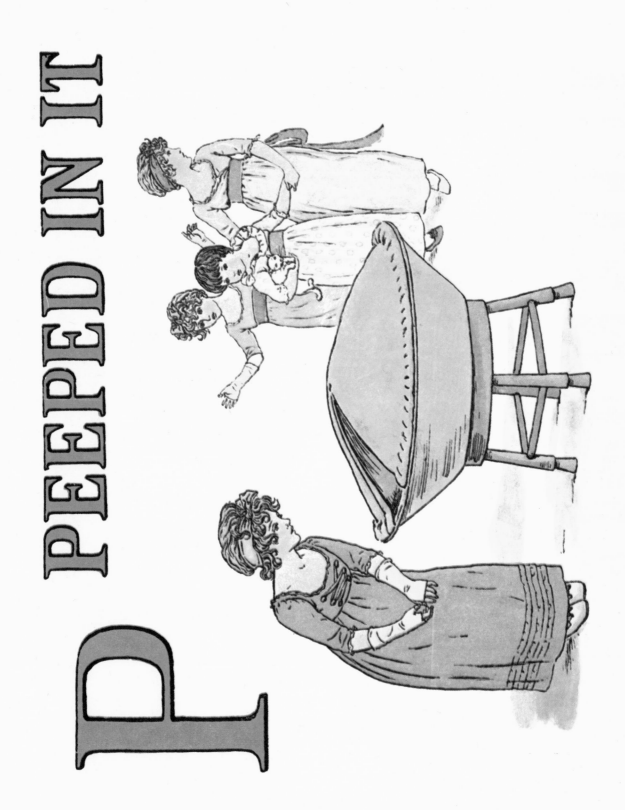

QUARTERED IT

R RAN FOR IT

S ANG FOR IT

I TOOK IT

UVWXYZ

ALL HAD A LARGE SLICE
AND WENT OFF TO
BED

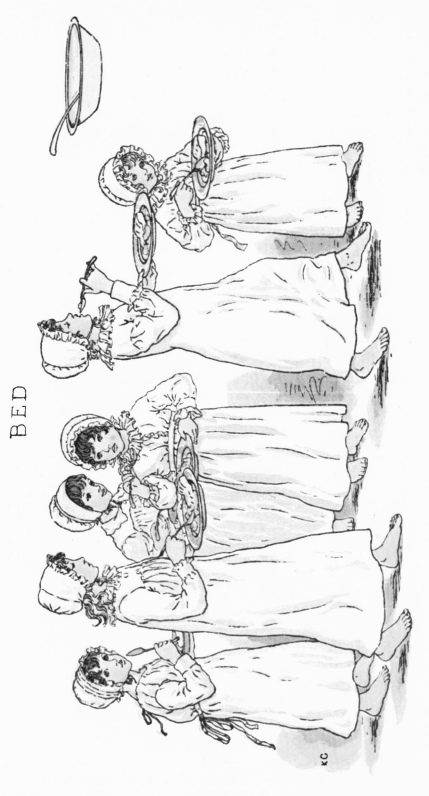

THE QUEEN
OF THE
PIRATE ISLE

by

Bret Harte

Illustrated by

Kate Greenaway

QUEEN OF THE PIRATE ISLE

I FIRST knew her as the Queen of the Pirate Isle. To the best of my recollection she had no reasonable right to that title. She was only nine years old, inclined to plumpness and good humour, deprecated violence and had never been to sea. Need it be added that she did *not* live in an island and that her name was "Polly"?

Perhaps I ought to explain that she had already known other experiences of a purely imaginative character. Part of her existence had been passed as a Beggar Child—solely indicated by a shawl tightly folded round her shoulders and chills,— as a Schoolmistress, unnecessarily severe; as a Preacher, singularly personal in his remarks, and

the Proud Lady.

Caught in a hurricane, Polly, her cousin Hickory, and Chinese boy Wan Lee reached a Desert Isle in the closet.

Changing into Pirates, they elected Polly their
Queen, and ran off into the California countryside. Joined by Patsey, a goldminer's son, they
decided to

slide down a mountainside to the mine tunnels.

The children stood before the mysterious darkness of the opening.

Inside they found the black-faced Red Rovers, actually miners in disguise, who lifted Queen Polly up to pay her homage. She and her Pirate Band had accidentally led them to discover the famous lost lode of Red Mountain. This was as good as a fortune to the miners and their families living on the Ridge, and all thanks to the Pirate Queen.

Polly slept, keeping the details to herself.

Editor's note: This is, of course, a drastic abridgment of the story.

Endpaper from *The Pied Piper of Hamelin*

THE PIED PIPER

OF

HAMELIN

BY

ROBERT BROWNING

ILLUSTRATED BY

KATE GREENAWAY

Complete text and illustrations

THE PIED PIPER OF HAMELIN.

I.

HAMELIN Town's in Brunswick,
By famous Hanover city;
  The river Weser, deep and wide,
  Washes its wall on the southern side;
  A pleasanter spot you never spied;
But, when begins my ditty,
  Almost five hundred years ago,
  To see the townsfolk suffer so
    From vermin, was a pity.

II.

Rats!
They fought the dogs and killed the cats,
And bit the babies in the cradles,

And ate the cheeses out of the vats.

And licked the soup from the cook's own ladles,

Split open the kegs of salted sprats,
Made nests inside men's Sunday hats,

And even spoiled the women's chats,

By drowning their speaking
With shrieking and squeaking
In fifty different sharps and flats.

At last the people in a body
   To the Town Hall came flocking:
" 'Tis clear," cried they, "our Mayor's a noddy;
   "And as for our Corporation—shocking

" To think we buy gowns lined with ermine
" For dolts that can't or won't determine
" What's best to rid us of our vermin!
" You hope, because you're old and obese,
" To find in the furry civic robe ease?
" Rouse up, sirs!   Give your brains a racking
" To find the remedy we're lacking,
" Or, sure as fate, we'll send you packing!"
At this the Mayor and Corporation
Quaked with a mighty consternation.

IV.

An hour they sate in council,
    At length the Mayor broke silence:
" For a guilder I'd my ermine gown sell;
    " I wish I were a mile hence!
" It's easy to bid one rack one's brain—
" I'm sure my poor head aches again,
" I've scratched it so, and all in vain.
" Oh for a trap, a trap, a trap!"
Just as he said this, what should hap
At the chamber door but a gentle tap?
" Bless us," cried the Mayor, " what's that?"
(With the Corporation as he sat,
Looking little though wondrous fat;
Nor brighter was his eye, nor moister
Than a too-long-opened oyster,
Save when at noon his paunch grew mutinous
For a plate of turtle green and glutinous)
" Only a scraping of shoes on the mat?
" Anything like the sound of a rat
" Makes my heart go pit-a-pat!"

V.

"Come in!"—the Mayor cried, looking bigger:
And in did come the strangest figure!
His queer long coat from heel to head
Was half of yellow and half of red,
And he himself was tall and thin,
With sharp blue eyes, each like a pin,
And light loose hair, yet swarthy skin
No tuft on cheek nor beard on chin,
But lips where smiles went out and in ;
There was no guessing his kith and kin :
And nobody could enough admire
The tall man and his quaint attire.
Quoth one : " It's as my great-grandsire,
" Starting up at the Trump of Doom's tone,
" Had walked this way from his painted tomb
       stone ! "

VI.

He advanced to the council-table :
And, " Please your honours," said he, " I'm able,
" By means of a secret charm, to draw
" All creatures living beneath the sun,
" That creep or swim or fly or run,
" After me so as you never saw !
" And I chiefly use my charm
" On creatures that do people harm,
" The mole and toad and newt and viper ;
" And people call me the Pied Piper."
(And here they noticed round his neck
A scarf of red and yellow stripe,
To match with his coat of the self-same cheque ;

And at the scarf's end hung a pipe ;
And his fingers they noticed were ever straying
As if impatient to be playing
Upon this pipe, as low it dangled
Over his vesture so old-fangled.)

"Yet," said he, "poor Piper as I am,
"In Tartary I freed the Cham,
"Last June, from his huge swarms of gnats,
"I eased in Asia the Nizam
"Of a monstrous brood of vampyre-bats:
'And as for what your brain bewilders,
"If I can rid your town of rats
"Will you give me a thousand guilders?"
"One? fifty thousand!"—was the exclamation
Of the astonished Mayor and Corporation.

VII.

Into the street the Piper stept,
　　Smiling first a little smile,
As if he knew what magic slept
　　In his quiet pipe the while ;
Then, like a musical adept,
To blow the pipe his lips he wrinkled,
And green and blue his sharp eyes twinkled,
Like a candle-flame where salt is sprinkled ;
And ere three shrill notes the pipe uttered,
You heard as if an army muttered ;

And the muttering grew to a grumbling;
And the grumbling grew to a mighty rumbling;
And out of the houses the rats came tumbling.
Great rats, small rats, lean rats, brawny rats,
Brown rats, black rats, grey rats, tawny rats,
Grave old plodders, gay young friskers,

THE PIED PIPER OF HAMELIN.

    Fathers, mothers, uncles, cousins,
Cocking tails and pricking whiskers,
    Families by tens and dozens,
Brothers, sisters, husbands, wives—
Followed the Piper for their lives.
From street to street he piped advancing,
And step for step they followed dancing,
Until they came to the river Weser
Wherein all plunged and perished!
— Save one who, stout as Julius Cæsar,
Swam across and lived to carry
(As he, the manuscript he cherished)
To Rat-land home his commentary:
Which was, " At the first shrill notes of the pipe
" I heard a sound as of scraping tripe,
" And putting apples, wondrous ripe,
" Into a cider-press's gripe :
" And a moving away of pickle-tub-boards,
" And a leaving ajar of conserve-cupboards,
" And a drawing the corks of train-oil-flasks,
" And a breaking the hoops of butter-casks :
" And it seemed as if a voice
" (Sweeter far than by harp or by psaltery
" Is breathed) called out, ' Oh rats, rejoice !
" ' The world is grown to one vast drysaltery !
" ' So munch on, crunch on, take your nuncheon,
" ' Breakfast, supper, dinner, luncheon !'
" And just as a bulky sugar-puncheon,
" All ready staved, like a great sun shone
" Glorious scarce an inch before me,
" Just as methought it said, ' Come, bore me !'
" —I found the Weser rolling o'er me."

VIII.

You should have heard the Hamelin **people**
Ringing the bells till they rocked the steeple
" Go," cried the Mayor, "and get long poles,
" Poke out the nests and block up the holes!

"Consult with carpenters and builders,
"And leave in our town not even a trace
"Of the rats!"—when suddenly, up the face
Of the Piper perked in the market-place,
With a, "First, if you please, my thousand guilders!"

IX.

A thousand guilders!   The Mayor looked blue;
So did the Corporation too.
For council dinners made rare havoc
With Claret, Moselle, Vin-de-Grave, Hock;
And half the money would replenish
Their cellar's biggest butt with Rhenish.
To pay this sum to a wandering fellow
With a gipsy coat of red and yellow!
" Beside," quoth the Mayor with a knowing wink,
" Our business was done at the river's brink;
" We saw with our eyes the vermin sink,
" And what's dead can't come to life, I think.
" So, friend, we're not the folks to shrink
" From the duty of giving you something to drink,
" And a matter of money to put in your poke;
" But as for the guilders, what we spoke
" Of them, as you very well know, was in joke.
" Beside, our losses have made us thrifty.
" A thousand guilders!   Come, take fifty!"

X.

The Piper's face fell, and he cried,
" No trifling ! I can't wait, beside !
" I've promised to visit by dinner-time
" Bagdad, and accept the prime

" Of the Head-Cook's pottage, all he's rich in,
" For having left, in the Caliph's kitchen,
" Of a nest of scorpions no survivor :
" With him I proved no bargain-driver,
" With you, don't think I'll bate a stiver !
" And folks who put me in a passion
" May find me pipe after another fashion."

XI.

" How ?" cried the Mayor, "d' ye think I brook
" Being worse treated than a Cook ?
" Insulted by a lazy ribald
" With idle pipe and vesture piebald ?
" You threaten us, fellow ? Do your worst,
" Blow your pipe there till you burst !"

XII.

Once more he stept into the street,
   And to his lips again
Laid his long pipe of smooth straight cane ;

And ere he blew three notes

(such sweet

Soft notes as yet musician's cunning
Never gave the enraptured air)

There was a rustling,

that seemed like a bustling

Of merry crowds justling at pitching and hustling,

Small feet were pattering, wooden shoes clattering,

Little hands clapping and little tongues chattering,

And, like fowls in a farm-yard when barley is scattering,

Out came the children running.

All the little boys and girls,

With rosy cheeks and flaxen curls,

And sparkling eyes and teeth like pearls.

Tripping

and skipping,

ran merrily after

The wonderful music with shouting and laughter.

XIII.

The Mayor was dumb, and the Council stood
As if they were changed into blocks of wood,
Unable to move a step, or cry
To the children merrily skipping by.

—Could only follow with the eye
That joyous crowd at the Piper's back.
But how the Mayor was on the rack,
And the wretched Council's bosoms beat,
As the Piper turned from the High Street
To where the Weser rolled its waters
Right in the way of their sons and daughters!
However he turned from South to West,
And to Koppelberg Hill his steps addressed,
And after him the children pressed;
Great was the joy in every breast.
" He never can cross that mighty top!
" He's forced to let the piping drop,
" And we shall see our children stop!"
When, lo, as they reached the mountain-side,
A wondrous portal opened wide,
As if a cavern was suddenly hollowed;
And the Piper advanced and the children followed,
And when all were in to the very last,
The door in the mountain-side shut fast.
Did I say, all? No! One was lame,
And could not dance the whole of the way;
And in after years, if you would blame
His sadness, he was used to say,—
" It's dull in our town since my playmates left!
" I can't forget that I'm bereft
" Of all the pleasant sights they see,
" Which the Piper also promised me.
" For he led us, he said, to a joyous land,
" Joining the town and just at hand,

" Where waters gushed and fruit-trees grew,
" And flowers put forth a fairer hue,
" And everything was strange and new ;
" The sparrows were brighter than peacocks here,
" And their dogs outran our fallow deer,
" And honey-bees had lost their stings,
" And horses were born with eagles' wings ;
" And just as I became assured
" My lame foot would be speedily cured,
" The music stopped and I stood still,
" And found myself outside the hill,
" Left alone against my will,
" To go now limping as before,
" And never hear of that country more!

XIV.

Alas, alas for Hamelin !
    There came into many a burgher's pate
    A text which says that Heaven's gate
    Opes to the rich at as easy rate
As the needle's eye takes a camel in !
The Mayor sent East, West, North, and South,
To offer the Piper, by word of mouth,
    Wherever it was men's lot to find him,
Silver and gold to his heart's content,
If he'd only return the way he went,
    And bring the children behind him.
But when they saw 'twas a lost endeavour,
And Piper and dancers were gone for ever,
They made a decree that lawyers never

Should think their records dated duly
If, after the day of the month and year,
These words did not as well appear,
" And so long after what happened here
    " On the Twenty-second of July,
" Thirteen hundred and seventy-six :"
And the better in memory to fix
The place of the children's last retreat,
They called it, the Pied Piper's Street—
Where any one playing on pipe or tabor,
Was sure for the future to lose his labour.
Nor suffered they hostelry or tavern
    To shock with mirth a street so solemn;
But opposite the place of the cavern
    They wrote the story on a column,
And on the great church-window painted
The same, to make the world acquainted
How their children were stolen away,
And there it stands to this very day.
And I must not omit to say
That in Transylvania there's a tribe
Of alien people that ascribe
The outlandish ways and dress
On which their neighbours lay such stress,
To their fathers and mothers having risen
Out of some subterraneous prison
Into which they were trepanned
Long time ago in a mighty band
Out of Hamelin town in Brunswick land,
But how or why, they don't understand.

XV.

So, Willy, let me and you be wipers
Of scores out with all men—especially pipers!
And, whether they pipe us free from rats or
    from mice,
If we've promised them aught, let us keep our
    promise!

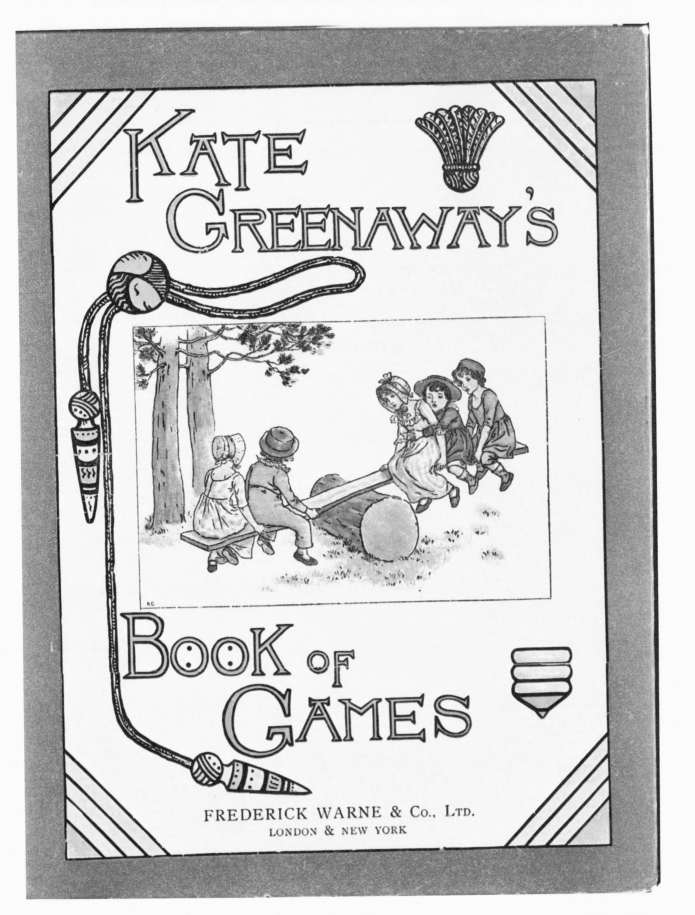

KATE GREENAWAY'S

BOOK OF GAMES

FREDERICK WARNE & Co., Ltd.
LONDON & NEW YORK

TOPS.

Tops are common enough objects to most people, but there is some skill required in spinning them. There are also many different games. For "Peg in the Ring" (played with a peg top), draw a circle about three feet in diameter. One player begins by throwing his top into the centre, and whilst it is spinning the other players peg their tops at it, but if it

Continued on page 313

SEE-SAW.

A GREAT deal of amusement may be derived from having a see-saw. It should be made of a thick plank of wood balanced over a fallen tree-trunk or other suitable erection. The players sit on the ends, balancing themselves as equally as possible, and go up and down. If one player will stand in the middle to work it, he can help to balance it and prevent a sudden jerk should anyone fall or get off without warning.

MARBLES.

MANY and various are the games which can be played with marbles "Ring-taw" is a very favourite pastime. Two circles are drawn on the ground, the outer one six feet in diameter, the inner one nine inches. The players put one or more marbles inside the inner circle, and shoot one at a time from the outer ring at them. As long as a player does not send a

Continued on page 313

HOP SCOTCH.

CHALK out on the ground a figure like the accompanying diagram Then the players "pink;" that is, throw their piece of tile, or lead, towards the pudding, or top of the figure. The one who lodges his tile there begins; if more than one succeeds in doing this, they "pink" again. The winner begins by standing at *, and throwing his tile into the division marked I; he then hops into the space and kicks the tile out to the starting point. Then he throws the tile into 2; hops into I, then into 2, and kicks the

Continued on page 312

SWINGS.

A SWING is a source of much innocent enjoyment which most children can have for a very small outlay. It consists of two upright posts, with a bar securely fastened horizontally; to this two ropes are tied to which a seat is attached. A bough of a tree is a more picturesque place for a swing, but trees are not always to be had for the wishing. Boat swings at fairs are irresistible attractions to most boys.

BLIND MAN'S BUFF

ONE child has her eyes blindfolded with a handkerchief, so that she cannot see, and is placed in the middle of the room. The Children say to her: 'How many horses has your father got?" She replies: "Three!" Children: "What colours are they?" She: "Black, White, and Grey!" Children: "Turn

Continued on page 313

KITES.

MOST boys and girls know how to make and fly a kite. On a fine windy day, what can be more delightful than a good run over a common or breezy hill. Even a wet day need not come amiss, it gives a good opportunity for mending them or for making new ones. Japanese kites made in the shape of birds are amusing novelties and look very

Continued on page 314

DOLLS.

M<small>OST</small> little girls like to possess a large family of dolls, though they may vary more in size and shape than an ancient Egyptian and a nineteenth century Masher. There are the tiny little dolls which lie in uncomfortable attitudes in dolls' houses decked out in bright

Continued on page 314

SKIPPING.

Two children each hold one end
of a rope, and stand so that in turning it just
touches the ground in the middle. How fast
they turn entirely depends on the skipper. Two
can skip at the same time over the rope if it
is a fairly long one. In skipping singly it is
more graceful to watch if the rope is thrown
backwards over the head rather
than forward under the feet.

SOAP BUBBLES.

MAKE a lather of soap and warm water, into which dip a clay pipe; blow through it, a bubble then issues from out the bowl — a wonderful transparent globe, glorious with iridescent colours.

tile out as before. He repeats this through the different numbers till he arrives at 8 ; here he may put his feet into 6 and 7 and rest himself, but he must begin hopping again before he kicks the tile home. He then goes on through 9, 10, 11, as before directed. 12 is another resting-place, where he may put down both feet. When he comes to plum pudding he must kick the tile with such force that it goes through all the other beds by one kick. In the other divisions it is not necessary to kick the tile so hard, as the player may hop as many times as he likes. If he throws the tile into a wrong number, or if it rests on a line, he loses his innings, whether kicking it out or throwing it in to begin with. He also misses his turn if he puts his feet down in what is not a resting-place, or if he puts his feet on a line, or kicks the tile outside the diagram.

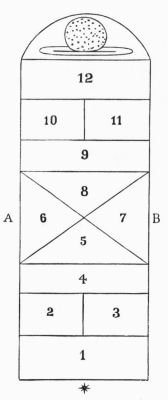

TOPS—*continued.*

gets out of the ring, and ceases spinning, the owner may pick it up and peg it at any others spinning in the circle. To set whipping tops going, they should be rapidly twirled round with the hands, and whipped, not too hardly at first. An eel skin makes the best kind of whip. Races can be played with whip tops, the boy who can whip his top along at the greatest speed is the winner. Another game called "Encounters" consists in the players whipping their tops against each other till one of them falls.

MARBLES—*continued.*

marble out of the ring he may shoot indefinitely. When they have all fired once, they shoot from the place where their marbles remained, not the original starting place. If a player drives a marble out of the circle he wins it and shoots again, but if his "taw" remains in he is out, and must put a marble in the circle. There are other games called "Conqueror," "Increase Pound," "Three Holes," "Lag Out," and "Snops and Spans."

BLIND MAN'S BUFF—*continued*

round three times and catch who you may!" Then then turn her round three times, and she tries to catch anyone she can; the one caught has to be next "blind man."

imposing. Paper " messengers " of all descriptions may be sent up the string ; as they speed up, turning rapidly round and round, they can be followed by the eye till they reach the kite. Parachutes are also easily made, but as no string is attached, they are not so readily captured again.

DOLLS—continued.

colours. There is the Dutch doll, with its stiffly-jointed legs and arms. There is the heavy old-fashioned wooden doll, as large as a good-sized baby. And now we have dolls which open and shut their eyes and say " Papa ! " " Mamma ! " Anyone who wishes to become a good needlewoman should try making dolls' clothes, where neat work is essential to the look of the thing.

BIBLIOGRAPHY

1871.   AUNT LOUISA'S LONDON TOY BOOKS: DIAMONDS AND TOADS.
        Frederick Warne & Co., London.   (10 ⅜ x 8 ⅛)

c. 1871.   Madame d'Aulnoy's Fairy Tales:
        (1) THE FAIR ONE WITH GOLDEN LOCKS
        (2) THE BABES IN THE WOOD
        (3) TOM THUMB
        (4) BLUE BEARD
        (5) PUSS IN BOOTS
        (6) THE BLUE BIRD
        (7) THE WHITE CAT
        (8) HOP O' MY THUMB
        (9) RED RIDING HOOD
        All published by Gall & Inglis, Edinburgh.
                            (6 ¹¹⁄₁₆ x 7 ¼ and 9 ¾ x 7 ¼)

1874.   FAIRY GIFTS; *or* A WALLET OF WONDERS. By Kathleen Knox.
        Illustrations by Kate Greenaway. Griffith & Farran, successors to
        Newbury & Harris, London. E. P. Dutton & Co., New York.

1876.   THE QUIVER OF LOVE: *A Collection of Valentines*. [By Walter
        Crane and Kate Greenaway.] Marcus Ward & Co., London.

1878.   POOR NELLY: *'Little Folks.'* By Mrs. Bonavia Hunt. Illustrations by
        Kate Greenaway. Cassell, Petter, Galpin & Co., London, Paris and
        New York.   (7 ³⁄₁₆ x 4 ¾)

1878.   TOPO: A *Tale About English Children in Italy*. By G. E. Brunefille
        (Lady Colin Campbell). With 44 Pen-and-ink Illustrations by Kate
        Greenaway. Marcus Ward & Co., London.

1878.   UNDER THE WINDOW: PICTURES AND RHYMES FOR CHILDREN. By
        Kate Greenaway. Engraved and Printed by Edmund Evans. George
        Routledge & Sons, London and New York.   (9 ¼ x 7 ¼)

1879.   THE HEIR OF REDCLYFFE. [By Charlotte M. Yonge.] Illustrated by
(*Another*   Kate Greenaway. Macmillan & Co., London. 1879.   (7 ½ x 4 ¾)
*edition
1902*.)

1879.   AMATEUR THEATRICALS. By Walter Herries Pollock and Lady
        Pollock. Macmillan & Co., London. 1879.   (7 ⅛ x 4 ½)

1879. *(Another edition 1902.)*	HEARTSEASE *or* THE BROTHER'S WIFE. By Charlotte M. Yonge. Illustrated by Kate Greenaway. Macmillan & Co., Limited, London. The Macmillan Company, New York. 1902. (7 ⅜ x 4 ⅝)
1879.	THE 'LITTLE FOLKS'' PAINTING BOOK. *A Series of Outline Engravings for Water-Colour Painting.* By Kate Greenaway. With Descriptive Stories and Verses by George Weatherly. Cassell, Petter & Galpin, London, Paris, and New York. (8 ¾ x 6 ½)
1880.	KATE GREENAWAY'S BIRTHDAY BOOK FOR CHILDREN. With 382 Illustrations drawn by Kate Greenaway. Printed by Edmund Evans. Verses by Mrs. Sale Barker. George Routledge & Sons, London and New York. (3 ⅝ x 3 ½)
1881.	THE LIBRARY. By Andrew Lang. With a Chapter on Modern English Illustrated Books by Austin Dobson. Macmillan & Co., London. 1881.
1881.	A DAY IN A CHILD'S LIFE. Illustrated by Kate Greenaway. Music by Myles B. Foster. Engraved and Printed by Edmund Evans. George Routledge & Sons, London and New York. (9 ⅝ x 8 ⅛)
1881.	MOTHER GOOSE *or* THE OLD NURSERY RHYMES. Illustrated by Kate Greenaway. Engraved and Printed by Edmund Evans. George Routledge & Sons, London and New York. (6 ¾ x 4 ¾)
1882. *(Printed 1882, published 1883.)*	LITTLE ANN AND OTHER POEMS. By Jane and Ann Taylor. Illustrated by Kate Greenaway. Engraved and Printed by Edmund Evans. George Routledge & Sons, London and New York. (9 x 5 ¹³⁄₁₆)
1883.	ALMANACK FOR 1883. By Kate Greenaway. George Routledge & Sons, London and New York. (3 ¹⁵⁄₁₆ x 2 ⅞)
1883–84. *(And subsequent editions)*	FORS CLAVIGERA. *Letters to the Workmen and Labourers of Great Britain.* By John Ruskin, LL.D. George Allen, Orpington and London.
1884.	ALMANACK FOR 1884. By Kate Greenaway. Printed by Edmund Evans. George Routledge & Sons, London and New York. (5 ¼ x 3⅝)
1884. *Other editions with different title, by F. Warne & Co.*	A PAINTING BOOK. By Kate Greenaway. With Outlines from Her Various Works for Girls and Boys to Paint. George Routledge & Sons, London and New York. (9 ½ x 7 ⅛)
1884.	LANGUAGE OF FLOWERS. Illustrated by Kate Greenaway. Printed in Colours by Edmund Evans. George Routledge & Sons, London. (8 ¹¹⁄₁₆ x 4 ⅝)
1884.	THE ENGLISH SPELLING BOOK. By William Mavor, LL.D. Illustrated by Kate Greenaway. Engraved and Printed by Edmund Evans. George Routledge & Sons, London and New York. 1885. (7 x 4 ⅛)
1885.	ALMANACK FOR 1885. By Kate Greenaway. George Routledge & Sons, London and New York. (3 ¹⁵⁄₁₆ x 2 ⅞)

1885.   **Dame Wiggins of Lee, And Her Seven Wonderful Cats; A**
(Second *humorous tale written principally by a lady of ninety.* Edited with
edition additional verses by John Ruskin, LL.D., and with new illustrations
1897.) by Kate Greenaway. George Allen, Orpington and London.
(7 ¼ x 4 ½)

1885.   **Marigold Garden.** *Pictures and Rhymes.* By Kate Greenaway.
Printed in Colours by Edmund Evans. George Routledge & Sons,
London and New York.   (10 ¾ x 8 ½)

?1885.   **Kate Greenaway's Alphabet.** George Routledge & Sons. London
and New York.   (2 ⅝ x 2 ⁵⁄₁₆)

?1885.   **Kate Greenaway's Album.** With 192 Illustrations within gold
borders. Printed in Colours by Edmund Evans. George Routledge
& Sons, Ludgate Hill. [Printed but not published.]

1886.   **Almanac for 1886.** By Kate Greenaway. George Routledge Sons.
London, Ludgate Hill, and New York.   (3 ¹⁵⁄₁₆ x 2 ⅞)

1886.   **A Apple Pie.** By Kate Greenaway. Engraved and Printed by
Edmund Evans. George Routledge & Sons. London and New York.
(8 ¼ x 10 ¼)

1886.   **The Queen of the Pirate Isle.** By Bret Harte. Illustrated by
Kate Greenaway. Engraved and Printed by Edmund Evans. Chatto
& Windus, London.   (8 ½ x 6 ⅛)

1887.   **Almanack for 1887.** by Kate Greenaway. George Routledge & Sons.
(3 x 4)

1887.   **Queen Victoria's Jubilee Garland.** (A booklet made up of
illustrations already published.)

1887.   **Rhymes for the Young Folk.** By William Allingham. With
Pictures by Helen Allingham, Kate Greenaway, Caroline Paterson,
and Harry Furniss. Engraved and Printed by Edmund Evans. Cassell & Company, Limited, London, Paris, New York, and Melbourne.
(8 ³⁄₁₆ x 6 ½)

1888.   **Orient Line Guide.** *Chapters for Travellers by Sea and by Land.*
Illustrated. The Third Edition, Re-written, with Maps and Plans.
Edited for the Managers of the Line. By W. J. Loftie, B. A., F.S.A.,
Sampson, Low, Marston, Searle & Rivington, Limited, London.
1888.   (8 ¹⁄₁₆ x 6 ⅜)

1888.   **Kate Greenaway's Almanack for 1888.** George Routledge &
Sons.   (3 ⅝ x 2 ⅝)

1888.   **The Pied Piper of Hamelin.** By Robert Browning. With Illustrations by Kate Greenaway. Engraved and Printed in Colours by
Edmund Evans. George Routledge & Sons, Glasgow, Manchester,
and New York.   (9 ¾ x 8 ⅝)

1889.   **Almanack for 1889.** By Kate Greenaway. Printed by Edmund
Evans. George Routledge & Sons, London, Glasgow, and New York.
(3 ⅝ x 2 ⅝)

1889.   **Kate Greenaway's Book of Games.** With Twenty-four Full-page
Plates. Engraved and Printed in Colours by Edmund Evans. George
Routledge & Sons, London, Glasgow, Manchester, and New York.
(9 x 7 ⅛)

1889.	THE ROYAL PROGRESS OF KING PEPITO. By Beatrice F. Cresswell. Illustrated by Kate Greenaway. Engraved and Printed by Edmund Evans. Society for Promoting Christian Knowledge, London, Brighton, and New York. E. and J. B. Young & Co. (8 ⅛ x 6)
1890.	ALMANACK FOR 1890. By Kate Greenaway. Engraved and Printed By E. Evans. George Routledge & Sons. (3 ⅝ x 3)
1891.	KATE GREENAWAY'S ALMANACK FOR 1891. George Routledge & Sons, Limited. (4 x 2 ⅝)
1892.	KATE GREENAWAY'S ALMANACK FOR 1892. George Routledge & Sons, Limited. (3 ⅝ x 2 ⅝)
1893.	KATE GREENAWAY'S ALMANACK FOR 1893. George Routledge & Sons, Limited. (3 ⅝ x 2 ⅝)
1894.	KATE GREENAWAY'S ALMANACK FOR 1894. George Routledge & Sons, Limited. (3 ⅝ x 2 ⅝)
1895.	KATE GREENAWAY'S ALMANACK FOR 1895. George Routledge & Sons, Limited. (3 ⅝ x 2 ⅝)
1897.	KATE GREENAWAY'S ALMANACK AND DIARY FOR 1897. J. M. Dent & Co., London. (4 ¹⁄₁₆ x 3)
1900.	THE APRIL BABY'S BOOK OF TUNES. By the Author of 'Elizabeth and Her German Garden.' Illustrated by Kate Greenaway. Macmillan & Co., Limited, London. The Macmillan Company, New York. 1900. (7 ¼ x 7 ½)
1882.	THE ILLUSTRATED CHILDREN'S BIRTHDAY—BOOK. Edited and in part written by F. E. Weatherly. With Illustrations by Kate Coleman, Kate Greenaway, Robert Barnes, Mrs. Staples, Miss Bennett, and others. W. Mack, London. 1882. (4 ⅝ x 3 ½)

MISCELLANEA. Illustrations in:

1868.	*The People's Magazine*	
1873–80.	*Little Folks.* Serial Story of 'Poor Nelly,' etc. etc.	(9 ½ x 7 ¼)
1874.	*Cassell's Magazine.*	(10 ½ x 7)
1881–2.	*Little Wide-Awake* (G. Routledge & Sons). Edited by Mrs. Sale Barker.	
1882. etc.	*Routledge's Christmas Number.*	10 ¾ x 8)
	St. Nicholas. *The Graphic.* *Illustrated London News.*	
1882. etc. v.y.	Routledge's *Every Girl's Annual.* *The Girls' Own Paper.*	(10 x 6 ¾)

Royal Academy Exhibitions:

1877 'Musing'
1878 'Little Girl with Doll'
1879 'Misses'
1880 'Little Girl with Fan'

1890 'Portrait of a Little Lad'
1891 'A Girl's Head'
1895 'Baby Boy'

Dudley Gallery Exhibitions:

1868 Kilmeny.
1869 The Fairies of the 'Caldon Low.'
1870 Apple Blossom—A Spring Idyll.
1872 (1) A Study.
　　 (2) A Reverie.
1875 Little Miss Prim.
1876 Little Girls at Play.
1877 (1) In Spring Time.
　　 (2) Dorothy.
　　 (3) Birthday Tea.
　　 (4) A Procession of Children with Flowers.
1878 (1) A Procession of Children.
　　 (2) Darby and Joan.
　　 (3) Miss Patty.
1879 (1) Prissy.
　　 (2) A Morning Call.

The selections in this volume from books written or illustrated by
Kate Greenaway have been faithfully reproduced with great care
from first editions or very early editions in the personal collection
of Edward Ernest. In most instances the type is the original
type, reproduced from the original pages; in the case of *Little
Ann*, however, the original Caslon type face has been
replaced by Electra. The Introduction, Biographical
Sketch, Artist and Critic, and Appreciation are also
set in Electra, a type face designed for Linotype by
W. A. Dwiggins. Color separations were made
by Magna-Graphic, Inc.; printing and binding
were done by American Book-Stratford
Press. The over-all design for this book
was created by Mina Baylis in the spirit
of Kate Greenaway's own books.